The Revelation - The Vision of Saint John, by Thomas Vathas. Monastery of the Revelation. c. 1596.

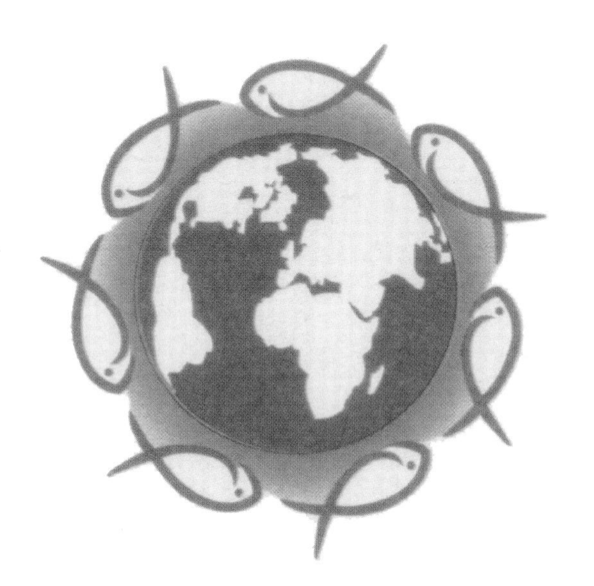

REVELATION AND THE ENVIRONMENT AD 95–1995

REVELATION AND THE ENVIRONMENT AD 95–1995

Patmos Symposium I

20 - 27 September 1995

Editors

Sarah Hobson
Oundle, UK

Jane Lubchenco
Oregon State Univ., USA

Published by

World Scientific Publishing Co. Pte. Ltd.

P O Box 128, Farrer Road, Singapore 912805

USA office: Suite 1B, 1060 Main Street, River Edge, NJ 07661

UK office: 57 Shelton Street, Covent Garden, London WC2H 9HE

British Library Cataloguing-in-Publication Data
A catalogue record for this book is available from the British Library.

Jacket photo shows Patmos, the monastery of St. John the Theologian.

REVELATION AND THE ENVIRONMENT AD 95–1995

First reprinting 1997 (J. W. Arrowsmith, UK)

ISBN 981-02-3238-1

Foreword by HRH Prince Philip, The Duke of Edinburgh

World Wide Fund For Nature

Office of the President

Avenue du Mont-Blanc
1196 Gland - Switzerland
Telephone : (41-22) 364 91 11
Telefax : (41-22) 364 54 68

I know that everyone connected with the World Wide Fund for Nature (WWF), and indeed everyone who is concerned about the future of the world's natural environment, warmly welcome this important initiative. I very much appreciate the honour of acting as co-Patron of this Symposium together with His All Holiness the Ecumenical Patriarch, Bartholomew I.

It is my firm belief that the health and vitality of our globe is the most critical and challenging issue of our times. Human communities have always tried to improve their conditions of life, and this has always involved the greater use of natural resources for food, clothing and shelter. They are also essential for transport, communications and cultural activities. Better conditions tend to encourage the population to increase, so the demand for resources becomes even greater. Meanwhile our planet Earth does not get any bigger.

Since Noah saved the living things of this earth in his Ark, it is perhaps apposite that this Symposium is taking place in a ship. Is it too much to hope that this might mark a turning point in humanity's treatment of its threatened biosphere?

The choice of the 1900th anniversary of St John's recording of the 'Apocalypse' as the occasion for a symposium on 'Revelation and the Environment' could not be more appropriate. Humanity is facing an apocalypse of its own making and it is only going to be avoided by the revelation of the facts of the critical situation we have created for future generations. It will also need inspiring leadership.

Philip

Introduction by the Scientific Committee

This book is the culmination of a remarkable symposium held as part of the celebration of the 1900th anniversary of the composition by St John the Theologian of the Book of Revelation, also known as 'The Apocalypse' and the last book of the New Testament of the Christian Bible. The symposium was held aboard the Greek car ferry F/B Preveli that transported participants from 20th to 27th September 1995 among the Greek and Turkish ports of Piraeus, Istanbul and Kusadasi. The journey ended on Patmos, the small Aegean island to which St John had been banished from Ephesus and where, according to legend, while living in a hillside cave, he composed the Book of Revelation.

Organised under the aegis of the Eastern Orthodox Ecumenical Patriarch, His All Holiness Bartholomew I, and the International President of the Worldwide Fund for Nature, His Royal Highness Prince Philip Duke of Edinburgh, the symposium brought together about 200 scientists, religious leaders, philosophers, economists, artists and policy makers to examine the nexus of religion and the environment. Thinkers and doers from 32 countries and representatives of the Christian, Muslim, Jewish, Hindu, Buddhist, Jainist, Sikh, Zoroastrian and Bahai religions participated actively in the discussions. The event was an important step in the long-running effort to find common ground among religious and scientific leaders who share similar concerns about the environment, but whose historical antagonism has often blocked collaboration.

In his opening remarks to the symposium, The Ecumenical Patriarch pointed out:

> the Book of Revelation is full of references to the consequences of evil for the natural environment. The ecological crisis, more than any other problem of humanity, reveals the truth that the world forms one unity and one community and that even the slightest violation of nature in one part of the world leads inevitably to consequences affecting the rest of the world.

Metropolitan John of Pergamon set the stage of the symposium when he declared in his opening statement:

> we are used to regarding sin mainly in anthropological or social terms, but there is also sin against nature, since evil upsets the created order as a whole. The solution of the ecological problem is not simply a matter of management and technicalities, important as these may be. It is a matter of changing our very world view. For it is a certain world view that has created and continues to sustain the ecological crisis.

These insights by religious leaders go hand in hand with a new awareness affecting science. Despite incontestable evidence of the worsening state of our environment and its grim implications for the future, scientific discourse appears insufficient to produce personal or social action on a significantly large scale. To the extent that religion, with its millennial tradition of access to moral and symbolic dimensions of humans, can espouse the accompanying imperative of scientific observation, it can endow society with a new vision that can lift science from its isolation as a social force and promote it into a materially-based pillar of moral and spiritual existence.

The symposium recommended seven 'Patmos Proposals' to guide future actions and initiatives taken by individual participants. This book concludes with those proposals.

It was no coincidence that the symposium was held at sea. Today's environmental crisis is nowhere more apparent than in the present state of the world's oceans. Covering about 70% of the world's surface, the oceans are a rich source of food, energy, minerals and medicines, which is growing in importance as terrestrial resources are becoming more scarce. The scientific evidence shows clearly that human influence on the marine environment is both extensive and increasing. The influence of human activities is felt in all parts of the oceans, from the most isolated beaches contaminated with oil and plastic litter to the ocean depths, which are used as dumping grounds for wastes we cannot or will not dispose of on land. In his Book of Revelation, St John urges humanity to 'hurt not the earth, neither the seas' (Revelation, 7:3). The anniversary of its composition provided a historic occasion to integrate current scientific knowledge about the oceans with the spiritual approach of the world's religions to water, particularly the world's oceans.

Conceived by a group of environmental leaders gathered on Patmos in 1988 and led by Metropolitan John of Pergamon, the symposium took form over seven years of discussions among theologians and scientists concerned about the steady pace of global environmental decline. Final plans for the symposium were put in place by a Scientific Committee, chaired by Metropolitan John, which worked for over a year prior to the symposium.

The Scientific Committee, and indeed the entire process leading to the symposium, was greatly assisted by a remarkable woman, Maria Becket, without whose vision, energy and organisational skills the symposium would have never occurred.

The Most Rev Metropolitan John of Pergamon
Professor Daniel J Amit
The Rt Revd and Rt Hon Richard J C Chartres
Dr Kriton Curi
Dr Mehmet Dülger
Dr Charles N Ehler
Bill L Long
Professor Jane Lubchenco
Dr Andreas A Papandreou
Professor David Pearce
Professor Christos Yannaras

Editors' Note

In editing the material emanating from the symposium for a book, we had a number of issues to consider. First was the choice of material. The academic papers which were formally presented in seven sessions during the symposium provided the most substantial content, but informal discussions which had been recorded on tape also provided some valuable thoughts and insights. We therefore decided to reflect the seven sessions with seven chapters and incorporate the more informal material into a final, forward-looking section.

Then there was the matter of length. Though the majority of individual papers were somewhere between 1500 and 2500 words, two papers were less than 1100 words, five were over 3000 words and two were over 4000 words - even though a limit of 1500 words had been set. There was also concern about the difficulty of including material that had been intended exclusively for a listening audience compared with material that had been carefully prepared as text for reading. Finally, there was the issue of language, since a range of English styles was used, including American English, English English, Indian English, and second-language English, not to speak of the difference arising from the language of various disciplines, for example, scientific, religious, philosophical and activist.

Each paper was therefore edited on the basis of a finished length of not less than 1500 words and not more than 2500 words; retaining the main arguments of the material; honouring the style and integrity of the piece; correcting ungrammatical English but not altering the type of English used; and standardising the different forms of spelling. The edited papers were submitted to their authors for comment and approval.

We would like to thank the following people for their assistance: Linda Sharp, Sally Morgan, Toby Mayer and Reza Shah-Kazemi, for their help in editing the material; and Lucy Walker and Sally Morgan for liaising with the authors and preparing the text for publication.

Sarah Hobson and Professor Jane Lubchenco

February 1997

The Symposium was made possible by

Sponsorship was provided by

COMMERCIAL
BANK OF GREECE

Support was provided by

SILVER & BARYTE ORES MINING Co SA

TITAN CEMENT COMPANY SA

Contents

Chapter 1

Interpreting the Book of Revelation: its meaning and relevance

Address of His All Holiness the Ecumenical Patriarch Bartholomew upon the Opening of the International Environmental Symposium at Sea

Welcome.

With the blessings of God, we have assembled like a scene from the Book of Revelation. We come from many cultural tribes, tongues, nations and faiths, but we share a common concern for the future of the planet and the quality of human life and relationships throughout the earth.

We are assembled on a kind of latter day ark, which is itself a symbol which would have delighted St John. As we begin our voyage, the ship confronts us with our essential interdependence. Here, in microcosm, is a truth which we need to bring to our thinking about the future of our world. If there should be a problem in steerage or distress in any part of the ship, the passengers dining in first class will not escape the consequences for long.

We shall be voyaging to Patmos on the sea of possibility from which life emerged. This is a time of profound cultural change and a moment in which we are mindful of the Spirit of God, which in the beginning moved upon the face of the waters and which continues to move.

We have been brought together by a memory. Nineteen hundred years ago on the island of Patmos, St John received the Revelation which forms the final book of the New Testament. This is not intended, however, to be a simple anniversary or an academic conference about an ancient text. Revelation begins and ends with the good news of the *Parousia*, the coming of Christ. At the climax of the New Testament there is no conclusion, but an opening to the work of the Holy Spirit in the future and the promise of a new creation: a new heaven and a new earth; a new community in a holy city; a river of life and a tree with leaves for the healing of nations. It seemed appropriate to celebrate this anniversary with a conference about our common home. St John's vision is of a united human family - every nation and family singing a new song.

Much of the Bible is addressed to those with ears to hear, but the Revelation to John is also to those with eyes to see. The story is told in symbols and archetypes.

The root of the English word symbol is in the Greek idea of bringing together fragments of truth to achieve a more profound understanding than would otherwise be available by analysis. Symbols help us to comprehend the relations between our sometimes fragmentary and fugitive perceptions of reality.

The great symbols are not devised to illustrate some thesis we wish to advance. They arise rather from some deep level of consciousness and are disclosed to our reason. They have the power to communicate in a way that generates energy. Two such symbols have been entrusted to our generation - the Cloud and the Globe.

In this year of anniversaries, we are all deeply aware of the mushroom cloud which, on the Sacred Feast of Transfiguration, August 6, 1945, opened a radically new chapter in human history. The cloud is a familiar symbol in the Bible, and although the mushroom cloud is reflective of man's transmutation, it should not be understood in an entirely negative way. For the first time in history, by unravelling some of the forces which lie at the heart of creation, we have acquired the power to destroy all human life on the planet. By the same act, the world community is under threat. The work which lies ahead for all those who love life is to transform this world community, which exists as an object under threat, into an object of promise and hope.

In practice, of course, we extrapolate and anticipate in a single act, which is one of the reasons why science and theology need to be in dialogue at this particular moment of transition. Symbols of the End-Time combine with what we consider possible to create a field of action and to fill it with either hope or despair. Science saves faith from fantasy. Faith generates the energy for a new world. We face a need to communicate in ways that release healthy energies for restraint and change. Moralising exhortations about the common good have limited usefulness. 'Mere appeals to ethical fraternity will never evoke in man that age old power which drives the migrating birds across the ocean' (Jung).

We hope and expect that this Conference will increase our understanding of the various ways in which we may perceive and engage with the world around us. Together, as Orthodox Patriarchs, Metropolitans and Archbishops, we seek your expert counsel, suggestions and input so that world-wide Orthodoxy can better contribute to the common front being forged by intrepid scientists, environmentalists and theologians who desire not only a pollution-free world, but a 'healing of nations' as well. Indeed, our common future depends on developing a way to perceive and participate in the world which will complement the analytical approach with an ecological awareness of elements in their various relationships.

The Statement of Orthodoxy and the Ecological Crisis published under the aegis of our predecessor of blessed memory, Patriarch Dimitrios, reaffirmed that the monastic and ascetic traditions of the Orthodox Church provide important insights for us. They develop a sensitivity to the suffering and beauty of all creation. 'Love all God's creation' urged Dostoevsky, 'the whole of it and every grain of sand. Love every leaf and every ray of God's light. Love the animals, love the plants, love everything. If you love everything you will perceive the divine mystery in things.'

It is a life-creating tradition, which beckons all to become new creations in Christ by being born of 'water and spirit', so that all matter, all life, becomes sanctified. For sanctification, *theosis*, to become real, there must be a *metanoia*, a changing of the mind, reflective of the sanctity of tears. It is not a mere poetic coincidence that a contemporary Christian poet describes the rivers, seas and oceans as 'a gathering of tears', bearing witness to man's adventure and struggling journey. So too, the Fathers of the desert considered 'the baptism of tears' as a lofty blessing empowering all men and women who seek 'to come to the knowledge of the truth'. Therefore, instead of asking for wisdom and strength and holiness, the angels of the desert asked for tears of repentance in their sojourn and struggle for salvation.

The ascetic tradition also offers a celebratory use of the resources of creation in a spirit of *enkrateia* and liberation from the passions. Within this tradition, many human beings have experienced the joy of contemplation which contrasts with the necessarily fleeting and illusory pleasure of treating the world as an object for consumption.

At the same time we would want to celebrate the resources offered by the international community of scientists and journalists. It is encouraging to recall the achievements of the Med Plan detailed by Peter Haas in his book *Saving the Mediterranean* (Columbia, 1990). It is easy to be cynical about the impact of scientific experts and communicators on the calculations of nation states, but the Med Plan and its development ought to reinforce the urgency with which we seek to build up a network of personal relationships at even higher levels. We hope that this Conference and its aftermath will serve as a major contributor to this growing family. The Orthodox Church is particularly well represented in parts of the world where 'the earth has been hurt,' to use a phrase from Revelation. In a perversion of science, would-be God-slayers have laid waste to great tracts of territory. In these countries, the experience of the martyrs which St John describes is also very pertinent. We pray that the energy which comes from giving up life for the sake of God and His Church will flow into a life-giving stream for the benefit of the entire community of mankind.

Another more recent symbol which points in this hopeful direction has sunk more profoundly into human consciousness. The earth-rise photograph taken in 1969 from the Apollo spacecraft shows the entire planet, sapphire-blue and beautiful, as no human being since the dawn of history has seen it. This angelic view is foreshadowed and enlarged in the Book of Revelation when John is shown the heavens opened and he sees a great multitude out of every nation, rejoicing before the throne of God.

It may be that the choice between life and death constantly being put to us by the Spirit is in our day being translated into a choice between one world or none. Theology and science ought to be partners in this work. We ought not to divide the one reality and seek, as one theologian has expressed it, 'peaceful co-existence at the price of mutual irrelevance' (J Moltmann, *God in Creation*).

We recognise however that many may have doubts about the possibility of traffic between the world-view expressed in modern science and the visionary material in Revelation. How can Revelation's vision of hope, sustained in the midst of passages portraying terrible destruction, be distinguished from a rather unconvincing whistling in the dark to keep up the spirits in time of danger and change?

One approach is to consider the various ways in which our many languages enable us to contemplate the future. We must distinguish between the *future* - that which is entirely constructed out of past and present, and which will itself become past - and the *future* which, beyond our control, will come upon us. In Greek, *ta mellonta* is what will be and *parousia*, which is frequently used in the New Testament, suggests a future coming. There is a similar distinction between *futurus* and *adventus* in the Latin languages derived from it.

Futurus suggests a future entirely constructed out of the past and present and, as such, it is a stimulus to planning. Futurologists of this school are those who rely on extrapolations from present trends. Often, of course, the collision between trends makes exact predictions difficult, but there is another problem with this approach to the future. Prolonging and projecting the present usually endorses present patterns of power and ownership and suppresses the alternative possibilities which the future holds.

Parousia alerts us to what is on its way to the present. In the Book of Revelation, Jesus Christ is hailed as 'the one who is and who was and who is to come' when the series might logically have been completed by 'him who will be'. A sense of the future as *parousia* stimulates the anticipation by which we attune ourselves to something ahead, whether through fear or hope. These foretastes, symbolic sketches and attunements are part of every perception of the unknown which we explore by reference to ultimate criteria such as happiness or unhappiness, life or death.

The climax of these celebrations will be the Holy Liturgy on Patmos. The liturgy is a work which binds human beings together in the Spirit of Our Lord Jesus Christ and liberates them to hope and work for His future coming in the world. Not everyone in this symposium shares the Christian faith, but we trust that we are all here around a common table like the Symposiasts of ancient times, because we all know that we are on the threshold of a new day. Conscious of the threat of nuclear destruction and environmental pollution, we shall move towards one world or none. We hope that we are assembled as those who are weary of defining their own tradition principally by excluding others. For many generations the Patriarch of Constantinople has occupied what is known as the Ecumenical Throne. There is in that title a reaching forward to the End-Time of the healing of the nations, when there will be communion between God and human beings in a new heaven and a new earth 'and there shall be no curse anymore'. We pray that this Conference may make a contribution to mobilising all people of good will in our world and bringing closer the day foreseen in the vision of Patmos.

May God bless one and all! Thank you.

The Apocalypse... A New Genesis

Roger, Cardinal Etchegary

The Book of Revelation sheds light on the problem of the environment not by its description of natural disasters but by its quiet and constant reference to Christ the Lord of history. As our environmental studies cruise makes its way to Patmos, we must let ourselves be guided by the 'Pantocrator' whom the Apostle John never ceases to set before us. I am delighted to contribute to this first session with the Anglican Bishop of London, Richard Chartres, and Metropolitan John of Pergamon to whom I am linked by more than twenty years of dialogue with Orthodoxy.

It cannot be repeated too often that the Revelation to John describes not the end of the world but quite the contrary, the new creation of the world. The first word of this book, the Greek word *Apokalypsis*, signifies 'revelation of what must soon take place' (Revelation 1:1). And what must soon take place is a 'new heaven and a new earth' (Revelation 21:1). Thus the first book of the Bible links up with the last, Genesis with Revelation. What they have in common is that both speak of Creation, but the one speaks of it at the beginning of history (protology) and the other at the end of history (eschatology). What merits our attention is that both of them, in the light of a double Genesis, are better able to help the little David that is humanity today to confront the gigantic challenges of nature and the cosmos.

The great tradition of the Greek Fathers, from St Gregory of Nyssa to St Maximus the Confessor, shows us at which stage the history of salvation encompasses both man the 'microcosm' and the cosmos the 'macranthropos'. Created in the image of God, mankind transcends the universe not in order to abandon it to its own devices but, on the contrary, to decipher its meaning through becoming its centre. We have signed a pact of sympathy and solidarity with the whole of Creation, visible and invisible, in spite of the torrent of violence that engulfs us. Every creature (and not only human beings) whether of the mineral, vegetable or animal realms, corresponds individually to a creative word of God. Our loving contemplation must encompass every living thing in a single glance. For Creation is an integral whole, like the Jerusalem hymned by the psalmist (Psalms 122:3). Yes, everything is 'bound firmly together', even if Genesis presents us with a God who takes his time to create. We need to nourish ourselves with the unitive vision of Creation. Nothing exists or lives of itself and everything is connected with everything else in relationships more profound than those glimpsed by the poet Baudelaire. The universe is not a simple back-cloth against which humanity should evolve according to the whims of a despot. For having wrongly understood or abused the word of Genesis which confided the management of Creation to it (Genesis 1:18), humanity ends up a victim of its own depredations and is only just beginning to measure the extent of the disaster.

Everywhere on the roads of Creation we encounter the person of Christ, the 'first-born of all creation, for in Him all things were created', according to the expression of St Paul in his Letter to the Colossians (1:15). Christ, the 'last Adam' (1 Corinthians 15:45), is prior to the first Adam for he pre-existed in the mind of God. The Adam of Genesis, the first to appear, is not the first; the second Adam, who comes after him, is the final *raison d'être* of the first and therefore constitutes his truth. The same name of Adam applies to humanity and to Him by whom humanity is fulfilled. 'First-born of all creation' - that means that we are caught up in the ascending movement, so dear to St Irenaeus, of 'Christ the recapitulator', which Paul has condensed in a phrase that is perhaps the most resplendent and most rousing of the whole Bible: 'All are yours; and you are Christ's; and Christ's is God's' (1 Corinthians 3:22, 23).

The Revelation to John underlines the original place of Christ in the history of salvation. But it never touches on the theme - so important in Pauline theology - of the reconciliation and recapitulation of the cosmos in the risen Jesus. According to St Paul, Christ was placed by his resurrection in a totally new relationship with the cosmos: from Christ in glory undreamed of energies shine out over all Creation. The Christ portrayed in the Revelation to John nevertheless has points in common with the 'cosmic Christ' of St Paul. The two sacred authors profess what has been called a 'christology of elevation', but what is striking in the Book of Revelation is the distance which is established between Christ and the cosmos. At the time of its Johannine redaction we are at the end of the first century, far from the fervour and enthusiasm of those first communities to whom the Apostle Paul, with a certain lyricism, presented the transfigured Kyrios. A tragic sound, almost a death knell, resounds over the world as the Revelation to John sees it. The vision which comes to us from Patmos is that of Churches caught up in torment and manhandled by satanic forces. It is about a vision, more dialectic than dualist, of Christ of the Apocalypse: on the one hand Christ is the Sovereign in front of whom the splendour of the deified emperors pales; on the other the same Christ is the Powerless one placed in check when the freedom of man and the malice of the demon block him with their refusal.

The Revelation to John is the great book towards which, as if by instinct, the thinking of the Church turns at every crucial (in the double sense of the word) stage of her history. It is to such a life-belt that Christians attach themselves when their faith is threatened in time of persecution. It is the true book of martyrs celebrating the test and the glory of all 'those who have washed their robes in the blood of the Lamb' (Revelation 7:14). In these times of trouble the faithful are nourished by the vision of the new Jerusalem described in the last two chapters, 21 and 22, which are inspired by the lavish and comforting visions of Ezekiel (cf. Ezekial 40-48). Beyond the definitive triumph of Jesus Christ over all the forces of evil, including death, the Revelation to John invites us to contemplate, or rather to participate in the eternal marriage feast of the 'new heaven' and the 'new earth'. The word 'new' emphasises the end of the book. The mysterious transformation in relation to the former order is more than a mere facelift; it is a real creation. A powerful trajectory shapes the story of Creation from beginning to end. God has the first and last word: 'I am the Alpha and the Omega' (Revelation 21:3).

It is important to underline - above all amongst environmentalists - that the new Creation does not define itself here by a sort of ascension to heaven of redeemed humanity, and therefore by the disappearance of the earth, but on the contrary by a solemn descent to earth. 'I saw the holy city, new Jerusalem, coming down out of heaven from God, prepared as a bride adorned for her husband. And I heard a great voice from the throne saying, 'Behold, the dwelling of God is with men...' (Revelation 21:2, 3). It is curious to note also that in this vision of a new alliance between heaven and earth, the Book of Revelation expressly eliminates the sea - 'and there was no longer any sea' (Revelation 21:1): the sea, a residue of the primeval chaos of the ancient cosmogonies was in the biblical mentality a pejorative element. If the Book of Revelation had been composed after our cruise, no doubt the vision would have retained the sea in the new Creation, for is not the sea the future of the earth!

Finally, still in the perspective of an ecological reflection, one should note that this new Creation is brought about within the setting of a new city, a new Jerusalem, in contrast to the first Genesis when God had created a garden for man who thus lived in the midst of nature. In the new Genesis there is no return to a golden age, to a lost paradise. God installs man in a city, which symbolises and synthesises the work of man. But the city, which until then had been merged biblically with Babylon, a point of crystallisation of human arrogance and power, is no longer the sign of the revolt against God. Taking the name of the earthly Jerusalem, which was its preliminary sketch, the new Jerusalem descends from heaven like a work that is absolutely divine; it has no need of a temple, 'for its temple is the Lord' (Revelation 21:22); it does not even have need of the sun or the moon to illuminate it, 'for the glory of God is its light' (Revelation 21:23). But, just as in the garden of the first Genesis, there is 'in the middle of the street of the city... a tree of life yielding twelve crops' (Revelation 22:2) a year, a sign of the abundance and the durability of the new Jerusalem. Certainly man, even in his glorified state, remains a creature, because Another has put his name on his forehead. But although constantly threatened in his finitude, he is also constantly endowed with new life for eternity, grace building on grace, as he receives 'the water of life without price' (Revelation 22:17). I find nothing more beautiful than this reciprocal relationship of love between the creature and the Creator that makes of eternity an eternal Genesis where God and humanity can no longer do without each other.

To you, too, participants in this symposium as we sail towards Patmos, I address the last phrase of the entire Bible, the Johannine blessing which is the epilogue of the Book of Revelation and is also on the lips of the Church of every age: 'The grace of the Lord be with you! Amen' (Revelation 22:21).

The Book of Revelation: is it Relevant to our own Time?

Richard J C Chartres

We live in a time of intense curiosity and anxiety about the future. This pre-millennial tension is expressed in the titles of some of the books on offer at international airports: *The End of the Future, The Foresight Principle, Framing the Future, Visions for the 21st Century.*

As we ponder the future we are also aware that the old order, established in that marvellously fruitful century the 19th, is coming to an end. For those with great investments in the old world order it is a time of anxiety and in some quarters there seems to be a deficit of hope as the future approaches.

It is unsurprising, therefore, that interest in the Book of Revelation has been rekindled in our own time. Over the centuries St John's work has tended to come into view at times of tension only to be eclipsed in more self confident periods. It has always been a controversial work and only secured an assured place in sacred scripture at a comparatively late date. In all periods there have been those who, like Luther the German Reformer, have said 'my soul cannot accommodate itself to this book'.

Despite the caution displayed by Church Authority, Revelation has always fascinated and attracted interpreters in times of anxiety. One of the major religious best sellers of recent years, Hal Lindsey's *Late Great Planet Earth* (Marshall Pickering, 1970), which draws heavily on the Book of Revelation has sold in excess of 15 million copies, and a genre of apocalyptic literature has flourished in its wake. A fascinating account of the cultural milieu which nourishes this apocalyptic enthusiasm can be found in Paul Boyer's book *When Time Shall Be No More* (Harvard University Press, 1992).

Apocalyptic sentiment is also expressed in some quarters of the ecological movement, which has transposed classic apocalyptic themes into rhetoric more accessible to a post-Christian generation. It is certainly salutary that we should be reminded of the judgement which falls on excess and irresponsibility and it is encouraging to be presented with a vision of a new world of sustainable equilibrium.

Occasionally, however, the bad news of pollution and other threats to the environment induce a rather triumphant gloom which is immobilising. Pessimism is often the luxury of the comfortable and it is a luxury which we cannot afford in the face of the real challenges to our life together on this planet.

Although 'apocalypse' has become a byword for unmitigated catastrophe, one of the most startling ways in which Revelation might have contemporary resonance is that in the last analysis it is not an 'apocalyptic' vision in the modern sense. Unfortunately it is commonly misread because we are sometimes more fascinated by the beast than by the lamb.

Receiving his visions in about 95 AD when the Christian communities in Asia Minor were suffering real and immediate persecution and danger, John unveils some terrifying scenes. Disasters are announced but they engulf only 'a third of the sea' (Revelation 11:13). There are always survivors, twice as many as those who perish. John's arithmetic is, like all his work, symbolic and needs to be read against the background of the Hebrew scriptures. In Isaiah and Jeremiah it is the small minority which is preserved. In John it is the majority.

For many modern people estranged from the tradition of the Church, these symbols are hard to construe. Revelation seems to be a happy hunting ground for individuals who have claimed the freedom to project their own fantasies onto John's text, undisciplined by any close knowledge of its context or allusions to the symbolic world of the Hebrew Scriptures.

Even without hidden polemical agendas, sheer ignorance of the most basic Christian symbols constitutes a formidable barrier to understanding the Book of Revelation. It is always salutary for a Bishop to be reminded of just how far much of the Western world has forgotten its Christian grammar. The Lamb is at the heart of the symbolic scheme of Revelation and the Good Shepherd is one of the most powerful Biblical pictures of Christ, endlessly reproduced in Christian art. I was walking up the steps of one of the churches in my diocese when I was hailed by a lively and intelligent 10 year old. Seeing me in my cassock carrying a shepherd's crook in the rather unpastoral setting of the inner city he very reasonably demanded, 'Who are you?' I pointed to my shepherd's crook, which is formed out of a ram's horn, and said, 'What's this? If you can work it out then you may be able to guess who I am.' He looked puzzled and then, examining the smooth curved horn, his face cleared. 'I know, you're the Grim Reaper!' He was referring to a cartoon character who regularly features on children's TV on a Saturday morning. We have to realise that the symbolic world, for a large part of the rising generation, has been comprehensively Disneyfied.

Given expectancy and some disposition to take pains, however, there is a treasure to be found here and the very difficulty of construing the symbolic language can open us up to an engagement with the visions which is more profound than would be the case if we were able to read them quickly and without difficulty.

We live in a world where few people are reached by carefully textured rational argument and in which sometimes superficial symbols are used to massage and excite our cravings. At the same time it is undeniable that pictures can mobilise public opinion in a way that is hard for rational argument to achieve. It is perhaps significant that the threat posed by CFCs to our atmosphere has been appreciated by the scientific community for some time but it was not until 'the hole' was identified that it become possible to communicate the gravity of the situation to the newspaper reading public.

In such a time, the handing on of a symbolic tradition is a significant endeavour. St John's work explores our imaginative response to the world, which is at least as deep and influential as any intellectual notions we may have about the world. Symbols open the possibility of engaging with truth at depth and this notion is crucial to the understanding of how Revelation might offer a gift to us as we respond to the challenges facing our generation.

There are distracting and perennial attempts to find the relevance of Revelation in dogmatic prediction, identifying particular symbolic figures with specific world powers and personalities of today while treating the numbers as modern statistics. This kind of interpretation is of course an unwitting tribute to the prestige of the scientific method as a way of arriving at truth. Such is the authority of this method that fundamentalists are always tempted to pass over traditional Christian Biblical exegesis, which in a disciplined way embraces imaginative and symbolic elements, in favour of restricting scripture to a series of objective events that can be given a time and a date and in which the participants can be photographed and numbered. John writes and reflects in the first century and there are undoubted contemporary references, including coded condemnations of the Roman Empire, as well as symbols that already had a long history in his own time.

At the same time symbols assemble truths which are often only glimpsed in a fragmentary and fugitive way. They are not to be confused with signs, convenient shorthand for some defined phenomenon. Symbols are given in a tradition but they reverberate with the depths beyond consciousness. They can unleash dangerous energies and they deserve to be handled with care within a community and a tradition of interpretation which can guard us from private fantasy.

John specifically describes his work as 'a prophecy'. 'In the Spirit' he uses and transforms the symbols in his milieu to uncover some of the recurring patterns of human history. These patterns include the tendency of state power to deify itself and the havoc wreaked by military and economic élites, havoc which is not only visible in history but which also devastates the earth and the sea. There is behind the work a sense of the coherence of the divine creation but there is also a glimpse of the reality and activity of evil at work, marring and spoiling creation. At the same time the power of the martyrs, those who suffer for the truth, is revealed. This vision is especially eloquent in a century which has witnessed the martyrdom of more Christians than any century since the Resurrection.

At the heart of the Revelation there is the conviction that in the Resurrection of Jesus Christ a new range of possibilities has been opened up. Revelation helps us to see the life of the present in the light of the future. This future is understood not simply as a projection of present trends but is anticipated as the coming of the Alpha and Omega, the 'one who is and was and is to come'.

The vision is grounded in a realism about the power and the presence of evil. There are terrifying scenes of conflict and a sense of the battle that is to come. But the denouement is joyful and the horrors are mitigated by visions of hope which intersperse the scenes of destruction. Again and again we look into a pit and then an angel speaks and draws our attention heavenwards. In particular we ought to note that the ultimate vision is one of the coming of the eternal world with people from 'every tribe and tongue and nation' participating in the reign of God. They shall not live as mere subjects but 'the Lord God shall give them light and they shall reign for ever and ever'.

It would be foolish to deny the authentic foreshadowing of the future in John, even if it is misconceived to view his work as dogmatic prediction with dates and times. More than that, prophecies which come from God have the power to make a contribution to bringing into being the future they envision. In the case of Revelation the plausibility of the hope revealed is enhanced by the fact that the posterity of the martyrs proved more enduring than the Roman Empire itself.

Although rooted in his own time, John exposes recurring patterns in a way that jolts the complacent but he also provides resources for encountering the future. These symbolic sketches, attunements and anticipations of the coming future can release energy in the present. Predictions easily induce complacency or hopelessness but John's eschatology opens up the possibilities of the future in which God, the first and the last, is coming to meet us.

It is easy to become immersed in our own time in a way which can cause us to miss the moment for decision. When we stand in the presence of eternity, as we do as readers of Revelation, the moment for decision is upon us. Profound change and energy rarely flow from analysis but more frequently from integrative vision. Revelation explores our imaginative response to the world which is at least as deep and influential as our intellectual notions about it.

The Church has often been frightened by this book. The caution is understandable if you see what wild spirits have made of it, but unless Revelation is taken seriously by the mainstream Christian tradition then it will be high-jacked by fanatics. Revelation opens up Christian faith to what God is doing in the future and it demands a response.

Revelation can make us sensitive to the transforming symbols which have been given to our generation. The growth of the environmental movement itself and the holistic aspirations which it embodies are hopeful symbols of a world which is learning that life depends on inter-relationships. Revelation helps us to appreciate that the web of interconnectedness ultimately depends on a relationship with the living God.

In conclusion, if I were to suggest that the Patmos Revelation is relevant in this or that specific way I would have falsified and neutered it. The historical situation in which we find ourselves is in many ways profoundly different from the circumstances of the first century. With the fall of the deified state, which was the paradoxical fruit of communism, we do not for the moment face in Western Societies a totalitarian ideology which claims a monopoly of the truth and seeks to suppress all rivals including the gospel. Instead, as Bauckman wrote in his recent *Theology of the Book of Revelation*, we face 'a relativistic despair about the possibility of truth and even more a consumerist neglect of the relevance of truth'. If churches are to have anything of value to contribute in such a time then they must, like the martyrs celebrated by St John, know a truth worth dying for.

Revelation warns us and it also diverts the pressure of this passing reality, to which we can so easily be confined, and opens up a future which is not simply a projection of present trends or a confirmation of present patterns of power.

For what it is worth, in reading and re-reading Revelation I feel my own agenda shifting, my complacency judged, my sense of urgency intensified and my hope enlarged of a world community in harmony with creation, assembled by the Spirit of God and flowing from the Resurrection of the One who spoke to John in a voice like the voice of 'many waters'.

The Book of Revelation and the Natural Environment

Metropolitan John of Pergamon

Nineteen hundred years have passed since, according to tradition as well as scientific research, the Book of the Apocalypse was written at the island of Patmos by St John. During this long period the book has never ceased to exercise fascination over its readers, both inside and outside the Church. This is due to the style as well as the content of the book. The style is marked by heavy and complex symbolism, which lends itself to uncountable interpretations allowing the imagination often to 'go wild', while the content refers to such upheavals in the existing historical as well as natural order that 'apocalypse' has become identical with the worst catastrophe that we can refer to.

All this explains a great deal of what Church history tells us about this book. The hesitation of the official Church to include it in the scriptural canon for many centuries is one of the notable facts. Another is the remarkable silence imposed on this book as is evident from the lack of Patristic commentaries on it for about eight centuries. Finally, the sudden and widespread exploitation of the book in the Middle Ages particularly in the West, to support all sorts of religious ideas, usually marked by fanaticism and extraordinary psychological manifestations, has given the book a mysterious character. Even among the orthodox of our time, in spite of the true spirit of the Orthodox tradition to be found in the Greek Fathers, a fanatical rhetoric is being spread among the faithful, particularly in connection with the number 666, that makes of the Apocalypse a terrifying and in some cases irrational text.

As an alternative to this frenetical approach, Biblical scholarship in the last few decades has enabled us to look at this book with more sober eyes. Thus, with regard to its symbolic images we know that they all come from Jewish prophetic and apocalyptic language and they are meant to cover up references to contemporary historical realities - especially ones related to Rome and its persecutions of the early Christians - so that the book might not provoke the wrath of the civil authorities. These symbolisms were therefore not meant to be 'mystical' in a 'Pythagorean' sense, but vehicles of communication among the faithful of the early communities versed in the Jewish tradition and in its later apocalyptic imagery.

The other important point that has emerged from Biblical research is that the main symbolic imagery of the book comes from the liturgical experience of its readers, particularly in the form of the Eucharist. One can say without exaggeration that the Book of the Apocalypse is a eucharistic liturgy or a commentary on such a liturgy. Without the liturgy this book remains incomprehensible or is seriously misunderstood.

Finally, it must be underlined that it is the theology of the book that matters in the end, not its symbolism. The book must be approached hermeneutically, that is, with reference to its diachronical existential significance. The book intends to put forward messages of ultimate significance for the life of the world, and it is to these that we must turn our attention.

What does the Revelation tell us about the ecological crisis of our time? We can only answer this question if we dig deep in the theology of the book. Some of its fundamental theological principles bearing directly on ecology are in my view the following.

History viewed eschatologically

One aspect of this principle is that all historical reality must have some *ultimate* significance. Nothing is wasted. Even evil contributes to the final purpose of history. It is a fundamental Biblical belief shared also by the author of the Apocalypse, that Satan is a servant of God's purposes; he is used by God to bring about the fulfilment of His will.[1] Later on in the Patristic period and under the influence of Platonism evil came to be regarded as *me on*, that is, a mere negation or absence of the good. But even then the belief survived that what happens in history, whether good or evil, forms part of a purpose which is to be revealed in the end.

The prophet - and John certainly claims to be a prophet - is given by God the charisma to reveal to us this ultimate significance. If prophecy makes no sense without history, since it is nothing but an interpretation of it, equally history ceases to be history unless it has a meaning, that is, unless it is somehow linked with prophecy.

This eschatological approach to history, therefore, involves an *apocalypsis*. This Greek word means an 'uncovering', or 'unveiling' - no doubt of the ultimate significance of historical events. Why did the term *apocalypsis* acquire the meaning of 'catastrophe'? Simply because the uncovering of many historical events, notably those of a negative character, will be marked by the revelation of their failure to prevail. *Apocalypsis* is therefore the final attempt of evil to impose itself on history as a reality, and it is this that makes evil so threatening at the apocalyptic time. The 'unveiling' of evil, historically often mistaken for good, is a necessary aspect of eschatology due to the factor of freedom. Freedom underlies all evil. This makes *apocalypsis* take the form of a real clash between good and evil.

Now the purpose of prophecy is not simply to satisfy foreknowledge, but to call us to repentance. Prophecy in the Bible is not to provide us with knowledge, but *to make us act*, by changing our attitudes and behaviour; it is like other charisms for the edification of the Church[2] and the world at large. Certainly this is the intention of the author of the Book of the Apocalypse.

History viewed cosmologically

One of the novelties of the Book of the Apocalypse is that it introduces cosmology into eschatology. It is commonly accepted that the Hebrew mind was conditioned historically, while the Greeks had a more cosmological interest. With all the qualifications that one should add to this general thesis, its main claim remains true. Judaism in its eschatology was interested basically in the final outcome of the history of Israel. The author of the Apocalypse, although brought up in this spirit of Judaeo-Christian apocalypticism, is also interested in the natural world, not only as a source from which to draw his symbolism but as a reality in itself. He thus describes the effect of the last days on the natural elements and he speaks of a 'new heaven' and a 'new earth' as part of the eschatological vision. This is extremely important. It introduces - for the first time - what we may call *cosmological prophecy* into the Judaeo-Christian tradition. A Christian is now called on to think of the Kingdom of God not only in terms of the salvation of the human being, but also in terms of the survival and wellbeing of the entire creation.

This did not prove to be an easy matter in the course of Church history. Already in the 3rd century AD Origen had put this eschatology into doubt by teaching that the material creation was the outcome of the fall, and that it is the spiritual world which will finally survive. Methodius of Olympus in the beginning of the 4th century wrote a treatise to refute this view and stressed the belief that God created the material world not in order to let it perish but to live forever. Yet about a century later in the West the great theologian Augustine saw the kingdom of God as a place where only human souls would exist, and the following he has enjoyed in this position has been persistent, at least in Western Christianity. By contrast, the cosmological dimension was stressed in the anthropology of theologians such as Maximus the Confessor (7th century AD) in the East, but the tendency to think anthropocentrally has also been observable there, even up to our own time. This anthropocentrism (we could call it anthropomonism) must have contributed greatly to the appearance of the ecological problem. It is of paramount importance for ecology that our Christian tradition replace anthropomonism with a cosmologically conditioned view of the human being, in line with the cosmological propheticism of the Apocalypse.

History and cosmology

One of the basic characteristics of the text of the Apocalypse is its universalistic eschatology. By the term 'universalistic' we do not wish to refer to theories of universal salvation or *apokotastasis*, but the simple fact that the author of the Apocalypse sees the ultimate significance of history as involving all peoples of the world. The 'Lamb of God' is presented by John as the only person worthy to unseal the book of history and reveal its ultimate meaning 'because he was slain and bought us for God in his blood *from every race and language and people and nation*'.[3]

The importance of this universal eschatology for our subject hardly needs to be stressed. The ecological crisis more than any other problem of humanity, reveals the truth that the world forms one community, and that even the slightest violation of nature in one part of the world leads inevitably to consequences affecting the rest of the world. The Book of Revelation with its universal eschatology unveils before us the ultimate solidarity of the human race and calls us to common action for the protection of the natural environment regardless of differences. In the end we shall all be one because the world in which we live is one.

The world is a liturgy

The Book of the Apocalypse is a liturgical book. By 'liturgical' we mean that it takes a view of the world with specific characteristics.

It is a movement, a dynamic reality. It is not a static reproduction of a fixed prototype as it was conceived by Platonism. It is neither recycled and reproduced eternally. Like the Byzantine eucharistic liturgy, it is a movement towards an end, a final purpose. Its natural resources are thus neither endless nor purposeless; they are 'sacred' in that they have a sacred purpose for which they exist. Each of its elements, no matter how small, is sanctified through the sacred purpose which lies within it.

It is a relational reality. No part of the world can be conceived in itself apart from its relation with the other parts. The world is thus like a picture, and this is how St John sees it in the Apocalypse, particularly in chapters 4-5. If you remove or destroy one bit of it, you destroy the whole picture.

It needs a priest, someone who will freely unify it and refer it back to its Creator. Man is the 'priest of creation', the one who is called to treat the world not only with respect but also with *creativity* so that its parts may form a whole and this whole may transcend its boundaries by being brought into relation with God. This makes the human being *indispensable* for creation. The axiom promoted by most ecologists that Man needs nature, but nature does not need Man does not have a place in a liturgical view of the world. On the contrary if we take seriously what natural science now calls 'the anthropic principle' we must give to the human being an indispensable role in creation. It is a role not only in the world's preservation but also its *cultivation* so that its ultimate meaning and purpose may be revealed (*apokalypsis*) through the human being.

Conclusion

These observations are not meant to exhaust the vast subject indicated. They are intended simply to underline some basic principles of the theology of the Book of Revelation, which in my view are of special importance to those wishing to approach the ecological problem at its deepest level. For it is my firm conviction that the solution of the ecological problem is not simply a matter of management and technicalities, important as these may be. It is a matter of changing our spiritual attitudes, indeed of *changing our very world-view.* The Book of the Apocalypse is pertinent to this task.

In the first place it calls us to think eschatologically. Unfortunately in our culture the eschatological outlook has been replaced by a present-dominated mentality. We have expelled the future from our way of thinking and we tend to exhaust our interest in what the world can offer us *now.* Apocalypse calls us to become future-orientated in our culture. This is extremely important for ecology.

Secondly, the cosmological outlook which Revelation introduces into its concept of history calls us to revise our understanding of sin. We are used to regard sin mainly in anthropological or social terms. But there is also a sin against nature, since evil upsets the created order as a whole. Cosmology must enter our ethic, and this calls for a revolution in our education, our sermons and our textbooks.

Thirdly, Revelation calls us to realise the universal character of the world's fate. The world is a unity and humanity is in the end but one. The slogan 'one world or none' is supported by the theology of the Apocalypse.

Finally, the Book of Revelation invites us to acquire a *liturgical* ethos in the broad sense of the term. We must behave 'liturgically', that is, treat the world as a sacred reality possessing ultimate meaning and entrusted to us not for consumption but for cultivation and protection of this ultimate meaning. We are priests and not lords or even managers of creation.

This is 'what the Spirit says to the Churches' at a time of ecological crisis. On our way to Patmos let us listen to the voice of the Apocalypse carefully. It is particularly relevant to our contemporary problems.

[1] *cf* The story of Job

[2] 1 Corinthians 12, 3

[3] Revelation 5:9

Chapter 2

Defining what is at stake

Introduction

Daniel J Amit

It is difficult to avoid pointing out the conjuncture that has brought all the participants together in this symposium: it is the coincidence of the sense of urgency for the state of the environment, the immense progress of science and technology and the current spiritual vacuum that corresponds perhaps to the end of the cold war. The words of St John summarise it well: 'Blessed is he that readeth, and they that hear the words of this prophecy, and keep those things which are written therein: for the time is at hand' (Revelation 1:3).

In consonance with the text of the Apocalypse, Chapter 1 introduced the spiritual dimension in this unusual exchange between religious representatives, scientists and environmentalists. Chapter 2 brings into focus two other components which are part of the great puzzle and which help define what is at stake: the politico-economic and the scientific. The politico-economic approach offers a picture of the powers that be, their perceptions of the crisis and the extent of their commitment to confront it. In this, there is almost no distinction between the political and the economic about how to handle socially, nationally and internationally the costs of dealing with a projected crisis. As Timothy Wirth says in his paper: 'It is time to retool our approach to national security - recognising that our economic and environmental futures are one and the same.' The scientists confront us with objective measures of the situation and provide us with a picture of what is at stake if the situation and the attitudes persist. Sir John Houghton reminds us that the climatic change that may occur by the end of the next century is 'more rapid than has been experienced by earth at any time during the last 10,000 years'.

The order in which the concepts of this symposium are presented, with the spiritual dimension followed by the combination of the politico-economic and the scientific, is a statement about the fact that the issue of the environment is principally *moral.* It is about what we are sacrificing at the expense of 'Our future and that of our children and grandchildren...because a sustainable biosphere requires a living ocean', as Professor Jane Lubchenco reminds us. It is about what the rich and the north enjoy at the expense of the poor and the south. This latter relation of cause and effect can be described with a metaphor of St John's: 'The waters which you sawest, where the whore sitteth, are peoples, and multitudes, and nations, and tongues' (Revelation 17:15) Moreover, as Dr Üner Kirdar points out, 'The longer these circumstances persist, the higher the risks and remedial costs will be.'

Nevertheless, the complexity of the issue is such that the religious sphere must turn to the scientific. Though science in the form of technology generates problems, it is also science that can pinpoint space and time. At the same time, science without the politico-economic sphere is ultimately relegated to the archives. Any scientific enterprise is fruitless unless science can impress its view on the sphere that solves social affairs. Science may be fascinating to listen to, but its implications may be 'bitter'. St John aptly illustrates this point: 'And I went unto the angel, and said unto him, Give me the little book. And he said unto me, Take it, and eat it up; and it shall make thy belly bitter but it shall be in thy mouth sweet as honey' (Revelation 10:9). Science has therefore to depend on the politico-economic sphere to sweeten the taste of its 'bitterness', or at least to address the issues it raises that are 'bitter'.

If the politico-economic sphere is to deal with the issues of the environment, it must undertake risks and costs, even when the risks are not immediately perceptible and not easily evaluated. Such an approach is usually beyond immediate political expediency, however loud the warnings may be. To use St John's words again: 'And I beheld, and heard an angel flying through the midst of heaven, saying with a loud voice, Woe, woe, woe, to the inhabiters of the earth by reason of the other voices of the trumpet of the three angels, which are yet to sound!' (Revelation 8:13). A strong sense emerges from the papers in this section that, whatever the risks and costs, the only way the politico-economic sphere can initiate action, rather than responding under pressure to a general disaster, is by calling on that sense of responsibility and adherence to moral values inspired by a spiritual approach. To use Sir John Houghton's words again, it is 'the need to care for the planet with all its living systems in a thoroughly responsible way'.

To conclude on an optimistic note, we recall that St John '...saw another angel ascending from the east, having the seal of the living God: and he cried with a loud voice to the four angels, to whom it was given to hurt the earth and the sea. Saying, Hurt not the earth, neither sea, nor the trees' (Revelation 7:2,3). 'And he said unto me, It is done. I am Alpha and Omega, the beginning and the end. I will give unto him that is athirst of the fountain of the water of life freely' (Revelation 21:6).

Our Common Responsibility

Timothy E Wirth

This is an unmistakably historic moment in time. The Cold War, which defined long-term security and national purposes for more than 40 years, is fast becoming a distant era. In its place we face a range of unfamiliar challenges every bit as demanding as those we have known since 1945. Freed from overriding fears about nuclear exchange and mutually assured destruction, we now face the prospect of ecological ruin and self-inflicted destruction by failing to comprehend and respond to the underlying threats to the planet's life support system.

The nature, diversity and speed with which these new challenges emerge dictate an urgent effort to understand the long-term challenges to international co-operation and to reassess the priorities for global leadership in meeting new tests and forging a better world.

As always, our interest must be in sustained peace and shared prosperity. What is novel are the diffuse trends that will determine those interests in the 21st century. I suggest that the key challenge we face is to transform the concept of sustainable development into a set of shared values and purposes.

Sustainable development fundamentally means that the economies of the world should attempt to meet the needs of today's generation without compromising or stealing from future generations. It is a concept rooted in the recognition of the mutually reinforcing nature of economic and environmental progress. And it is within this notion of interdependence that we can discern the enormous magnitude of this challenge. Ecological systems are the very foundation of modern society - in science, in agriculture, in social and economic planning. Over the long-term, living off our ecological capital is a bankrupt economic strategy. At the same time, most people and nations aspire to economic growth and scientific and technological progress, which in turn are the essential building blocks of environmental protection.

For far too long, concern about the environment has been regarded as a peripheral issue that can be treated as luxury in the context of prosperity. The fact is that the economy is inextricably tied to the environment and totally dependant upon it.

Five biological systems - croplands, forests, grasslands, oceans and fresh waterways - support the world economy. Except for fossil fuels and minerals, they supply all the raw materials for industry and provide all our food.

All economic activity is dependent on the environment and its underlying resource base. When the environment is finally forced to file for bankruptcy because its resource base has been polluted, degraded, dissipated, irretrievably compromised, then the economy goes into bankruptcy with it. Lost too, is the basis for meeting human needs, promoting social justice and harnessing our faith - the foundation for our compassion, kindness, stewardship and humanity.

We are already seeing the horrific implications of lost humanity that accompanies human deprivation, diminishing resources, destroyed environments and lost opportunity. They are apparent in many of today's trouble spots from Haiti and Somalia to the Sudan and Rwanda. Moreover, our deficit spending of environmental capital has a direct, measurable impact on human security, justice and peace. This truth is reflected in the suffering of 2 billion human beings living in wretched poverty; the hunger that stalks 800 million men, women and children; the 20-30 million people infected by HIV; the combination of violence, poverty and environmental degradation that today places more than 20 million people in the ranks of the world's refugees.

The security of all nations is inextricably linked to these trends - hinging upon whether we can strike a sustainable, equitable balance between human numbers and the planet's capacity to support life.

Two trends override all others in driving the unsustainable course we are on. First, is the exponential growth of the human population. During my lifetime, world population has nearly tripled. Every year, the world gains another 91 million inhabitants. Ninety-five per cent of that growth is taking place in the impoverished countries of the developing world, where for man the question of survival is weighed in the resources and sustenance that is available for immediate consumption.

Poor people in Asia, Africa and Latin America are in desperate need of fuel and land to work. Their needs and their numbers makes them unwitting, but powerful agents of destruction whether in tropical rain forests or on fragile hillsides, a tragedy for the environment, and their own futures.

The industrialised world is growing slowly by comparison, but the lifestyle, technology and consumptive capacity have been developed to utilise resources and produce wastes at a staggering rate. Comprising only one-fifth of the world's population, the industrialised countries consume two-thirds of all resources and generate four-fifths of all pollutants and wastes. In addition, the appetite of the affluent for timber products is just as much of a menace to forests in Malaysia, Indonesia, the Philippines, Brazil and the United States.

The bulk of the underground water being drained away from our future flows into the shining cities of the 'haves', not the parched lands of the 'have-nots' and those same cities are, of course, the furnaces of global warming.

None of this is news. The sciences have allowed us to accumulate an invaluable record about how our environment works and why it is essential to our long-term prosperity. Yet the curious fact is that we refuse to believe or respond to it.

Nonetheless, the scientific community bears great responsibility and has an enormous opportunity for alerting the public and government leaders to emerging problems. Scientists warned about the dangers of ozone depletion long before the ozone hole developed over Antarctica and public policy moved dramatically forward.

At the same time, we must recognise the limits of science in some of these areas. Rooted, as it is, in the irreducible properties of the natural world, science does not, and cannot, always provide a simple answer. Ranges of uncertainty - which we are accustomed to in economic policy making - must be accepted in these new priorities for human endeavour. We must act in a precautionary manner, guided by principles of stewardship, justice and concern.

That is where the religious community - our moral leadership - must come in. The world is desperately in need of a new set of shared global values - common purposes grounded in ethical principles of justice and stewardship. Scientists, policy makers and religious communities alike sorely need what theologians must now provide - a positive vocabulary of human limit and justice in a sanctified and sustainable creation.

Individually and collectively, the peoples of the world need to forge common cause and set priorities for realising the double dividends of sustainable development: progress toward environmental balance and economic development.

What then should our agenda for the future look like?

Population must be at the top of the agenda for sustainable development. Unchecked, the spiral of population growth will cast a pall over every environmental endeavour. Fortunately we have a remarkable agenda - agreed at Cairo - that reflects basic values and comprehensive efforts for addressing rapid demographic change - from making family planning and reproductive health services universally available to sharply expanding the education of girls and focusing on child survival, strong families and the engagement of grassroots, non-governmental organisations.

Next on the agenda is the promotion of the social, political and economic rights of women so that we enter the 21st century free of gender discrimination. The return, in terms of stability, environmental quality and economic productivity, will outweigh the costs for generation after generation.

Then comes the provision of basic health services. The elimination of four major, easily preventable diseases - measles, tetanus, whooping cough and polio - plus the eradication of iodine and vitamin A deficiencies together with the global availability of oral rehydration therapy are all achievable early in the next century at relatively little global cost. These measures alone would save 3-4 million lives annually and perhaps eliminate upwards of 20 million early childhood deaths.

We also need to get the prices right. Nations, including the United States, can no longer assume that they bear no cost for fouling the air or depleting our resources. Instead, ways must be found to internalise those costs and allow the marketplace to help determine the most efficient means of achieving our environmental goals.

We must face the challenge of governing in the 21st century. Traditionally we have assumed that our relationships with the rest of the world were like a hub and a spoke; we are the hub in Washington, and individual spokes go out to capitals around the world - to London, Delhi, Tokyo or Bogota. The value of broader, operative international alliances and organisations and the rapidly growing network of private, non-governmental, voluntary organisations must now be acknowledged.

Global climate change, ozone depletion, biodiversity, refugees, narcotics have become concerns which challenge us all and must be dealt with through stronger multilateral, co-operative organisations. Changing the consciousness of individuals and forging common cause among institutions will not be easy but we have a rich, if complicated framework from which to build, beginning with the United Nations, which must be reformed to make sustainable development among its most basic missions for the 21st century.

The challenge of governance also goes down, to the great wave of individuals who have been far ahead of government in recognising the challenge of sustainable development. The phenomenal growth of non-governmental organisations (NGOs) around the world is one of the salient features of our time. The OECD counted over 2,500 NGOs among its 24 countries in 1990, up from 1,600 a decade before. But that is nothing compared to NGO growth in the developing world. Roger Riddell of the Overseas Development Institute suggests there may be 25,000 grassroots organisations in one Indian state, Tamil Nadu.

The heroes of the Earth Summit in Rio were not the heads of State, but the NGOs who defined and drove Agenda 21. Women's groups from around the world played a leading role in the organisation and agenda at the UN Human Rights Conference held in 1993 in Vienna; at the Cairo Conference again last fall; and most powerfully at the Beijing Conference that concluded two weeks ago. The challenge for those who presume to govern is to enlist and engage the sensitivity, enthusiasm and creativity that grassroots groups offer.

We have a real opportunity in terms of preserving and utilising our biological inheritance. Compounds of undiscovered promise await us - already more than 50 per cent of today's top selling pharmaceuticals come directly from plant biochemicals. Similarly, our food base comes from the reservoir of nature; just three species of grass - rice, wheat and corn - have become humanity's principal foods. As with plants possessing medical potential, we have barely begun to understand the abundance of the natural world. Certainly this is the overwhelmingly important frontier of the future in which we can prospect for food, fuel, pharmaceuticals or fibre as we once prospected for gold and silver here in our own backyard.

To conclude, in the newly configured world, national security is closely linked to human security. Human security is built on a foundation of peace and political stability, physical health and economic well being. The primary threats to human security may not be as easy to recognise as, say, an enemy's nuclear arsenal, but they are no less deadly.

All around the globe we are coming to understand the close connections between poverty, the environment, the economy and security. This historic transformation demands that we now liberate ourselves - from outworn policies, from old assumptions, from fixed views that only yesterday seemed to be the dividing and defining lines of our politics.

Crisis prevention and the challenge of sustainable development are among the great challenges for the remainder of this and into the next century. It is time to retool our approach to national security - recognising that our economic and environmental futures are one and the same. And it is these challenges which will determine the future we leave to our children and grandchildren.

Climate Change, Global Warming and the Oceans

John Houghton

Climate change

Since the last Ice Age, generations of human beings have organised their activities to take advantage of locally available resources of food, fuel, fibre and forage. Human settlements, their agriculture, water use and commercial activities have adapted to the current climate (that is, temperature and rainfall) and its variability. Any large, rapid change in climate will affect these activities and the resources on which they depend and will require rapid, and probably costly, adaptation to re-establish the match between climatic resources and human needs.

Climate extremes are an important manifestation of the natural variability of climate. During recent decades, different parts of the world have experienced extreme temperatures, record floods, droughts and windstorms. There is no strong evidence that these weather events are outside the natural range of climate variability of the last few centuries. However, their impact serves to emphasise the vulnerability of human communities to climate variations and extremes. In particular, during the later years of the 1980s and the 1990s, the insurance industry has experienced unparalleled losses due to extreme weather events, providing a good illustration of this increased vulnerability.

Significant climate change is expected over the next century because of the increase in greenhouse gases (especially carbon dioxide and methane) which is occurring as a result of human activities (especially fossil fuel burning and deforestation). This increase is leading to an overall warming of the earth's surface such that, if no environmental pressures or controls are introduced, an increase in global mean temperature of about 2.5 degrees centigrade (ranging from 1.5 to 4 degrees centigrade) can be expected by the year 2100. This would represent a change of climate more rapid than has been experienced by the Earth at any time during the last 10,000 years.

Estimation of the likely future climate change is made complicated because of the effects of anthropogenic aerosols (microscopic particles in the atmosphere), which originate particularly from the sulphur-containing gases emitted from power stations - effluents which also give rise to the acid rain problem. These aerosols reflect sunlight and so tend to cool the Earth's surface. However, they are very short-lived (a few days), so that they are concentrated near industrial regions. Nevertheless, their effects on the climate, even quite far away from these regions, can be considerable. Because of the acid rain problem, emissions of sulphur-containing gases are being severely controlled, especially in North America and Europe. However, they are growing rapidly in Asia, although controls can also be expected there in due course.

In making detailed predictions of climate change, the influences of both the atmosphere and the oceans have to be taken into account. In climate models the circulations of the atmosphere and the oceans are coupled together in a sophisticated manner. Of particular interest and concern are changes in the oceans over long time scales (several hundred years or more) which could occur as a result of anthropogenic influences and which could have substantial effects on the climate.

The impacts of climate change

The main impacts of the expected climate change are a rise in sea level and changes in rainfall and temperature extremes.

The expected rise in sea level of about 0.5m (ranging from 0.2m to 1m) by the year 2100 arises mostly from the expansion of water in the oceans because of the increased temperature and from the melting of glaciers; the contribution from changes in the ice sheets in the Arctic and Antarctic is expected to be small. Adaptation, at a cost, to such a rise will be possible in many coastal regions. However, adaptation will be extremely difficult, if not impossible, in some particularly vulnerable areas such as the delta regions of large rivers in Bangladesh, Egypt and Southern China and the many low-lying islands in the Indian and Pacific Oceans. The situation in many of these areas will be exacerbated because the land is sinking at a similar rate to the rise in the water levels expected from global warming. This is for reasons such as tectonic movement and the extraction of ground water. Substantial loss of land will occur in these areas and many millions of people are likely to be displaced (for instance, 6 million live below the 1m contour in Bangladesh).

The changes in rainfall are likely to be manifested particularly through increased incidences of both droughts and floods in some places. For instance, in continental areas at mid-latitudes in the Northern Hemisphere - for example in North America and Southern Europe - summers are likely to be warmer with increased evaporation from the surface and possibly with less average rainfall; drought conditions can therefore be expected to occur more frequently and may sometimes be more prolonged. In Southern Asia more intense monsoons can be expected, with increased tendency to flooding (although if large anthropogenic aerosol concentrations were present over Asia, this effect could be reduced). As the demand for water increases in nearly every country, substantial tensions can be expected, especially in regions where the water from major river systems is shared between nations. The Secretary General of the UN has suggested that wars in the future are likely to be about water rather than oil.

Studies of global food supplies in a globally warmed world tend to suggest that the global quantity of available food supply might not be affected by very much - some regions might be able to grow more while others grow less. However, the regions likely to be most affected by reduced food production are those in developing countries in the sub-tropics where there are rapidly growing populations. In the areas most seriously affected there could be large numbers of environmental refugees.

Other impacts of the likely climate change are on human health (increased heat stress and more widespread vector borne diseases such as malaria) and on the health of some ecosystems such as forests which will not be able to adapt rapidly enough to match the rate of climate change.

These impacts of anthropogenic climate change will generate substantial social and political implications, and also implications for world security. Of particular concern are some developing countries which will be substantially disadvantaged and in which a large number of environmental refugees will be created (studies have suggested 150 million by the middle of next century).

Action regarding climate change

The scientists of the world involved with climate and climate change have worked together through the Intergovernmental Panel on Climate Change (IPCC), formed in 1988 to present policy-makers with their best information regarding the future climate. I was privileged to chair the Scientific Assessment of the IPCC which was agreed and published in 1990. Despite the substantial uncertainties in future predictions, a wide consensus was achieved by the world scientific community regarding the Assessment's findings. Assisted by that scientific consensus, a Framework Convention on Climate Change was agreed at the Earth Summit in Río in 1992. Its objective, stated in Article 2, puts action regarding climate change in the context of sustainable development. It states:

> The ultimate objective of this Convention . . . is to achieve . . . stabilisation of greenhouse gas concentrations in the atmosphere at a level that would prevent dangerous anthropogenic interference with the climate system. Such a level should be achieved within a time frame sufficient to allow ecosystems to adapt naturally to climate change, to ensure that food production is not threatened and to enable economic development to proceed in a sustainable manner.

To find the best way to meet the demands of this objective will require a great deal of debate and discussion, based on the best scientific and technical information, across all scientific (including social scientific) disciplines.

The actions required to mitigate the effects of global warming are to increase the processes which remove carbon dioxide from the atmosphere (for example by reducing deforestation and increasing afforestation) and to reduce the emissions of both carbon dioxide and methane from anthropogenic sources (for example by increasing energy efficiency and by the development of energy sources which have much lower carbon dioxide emissions).

The science of global warming and climate change is very complex and involves frontier regions of science and technology (such as the dynamics of non-linear chaotic systems, the development of complex models, space observation, large-scale data handling and management systems). It is also probably the area of science where the greatest interaction is currently occurring between the international scientific community and the world political arena. It is therefore a very demanding, exposed and exciting area of science in which to be involved. The further challenge to humanity is to face the need to care for the planet with all its living systems in a thoroughly responsible way.

Managing in an Era of Uncertainty

Üner Kirdar

Far-reaching and profound transformations are taking place in the perceptions and structures of the world's politics, economics, demography, technology, ecology and ethics; societies must now evaluate these changes and must make the necessary adjustments.

There are over five billion people on the earth today, up from two billion at the beginning of the century. The world's population is increasing by a quarter of a million people every day and is now spread over every habitable part of the globe. We use more energy, more technology, more food, water and raw materials than all those who have lived before us.

In some parts of the world, entire societies have risen to levels of unprecedented affluence. Yet millions of people continue to live in poverty, endure hunger, suffer from many preventable diseases and die young. Some developing countries have improved growth and have coped with change. Most others have experienced a decline in growth rates and living standards and have suffered from even greater poverty than hitherto.

Despite - or perhaps even because of - this diversity in achievement, nations are becoming increasingly interdependent and the world is increasingly confronted with issues that affect mankind as a whole. They range from economic requirements to social needs, from energy to the protection of the world's ecology including its oceans, from information to new discoveries, and they call for joint policy action. Peace and security cannot be achieved unless international co-operation is also extended to deal with the threats that stem from failures in development, from environmental degradation and from lack of progress towards ensuring tangible human development.

There is now a growing awareness among scientists and policy-makers that sustaining the environment is inextricably linked with eliminating global poverty. Yet in many instances, environmental considerations are still regarded as constraints to development or vice versa.

At present, the major reason for the continuing deterioration of the world ecology and environment is the unsustainable patterns of production and consumption, particularly in industrialised countries. In developing countries, the persistence of poverty and restricted economic opportunities are the main sources of deterioration in the physical environment. Environmental protection in developing countries must, therefore, be viewed as an integral part of the development process.

As the twentieth century comes to a close, not only are the number of people and their activities vastly increasing, but major unintended global ecological changes are also occurring.

Between 1950 and 1980, the world economy grew threefold, as did the consumption of fossil fuels. The amount of carbon dioxide in the atmosphere increased by 25%. About 95% of the total global carbon dioxide in the atmosphere is at present caused by the combustion of fossil fuels, consumed mostly by the industrialised countries. It is estimated that this consumption, which is nearly two billion tons per annum, may rise to over ten billion tons during the next millennium. As a result of this trend, it is also expected that, by the year 2050, the average temperature of the earth may rise in the range of 1.5 °C to 4.5 °C. Such an increase is regarded to be sufficient to cause a major world-wide climatic change, which could further exacerbate the existing problems of drought, desertification, soil erosion, tropical cyclones and floods and could hamper the prospective economic growth of many countries.

Another consequence of global warming and climate change is the expansion of the oceans, with a resulting rise in sea levels of a magnitude of 1.4 to 2.2 metres. Since nearly one third of the world's population lives within 60 kilometres of a coastline, such an occurrence would have a profound impact on patterns of agricultural growth, industry, transport and habitation. The most adverse effects of global warming will be felt in the least developed countries, on lower-income groups, on residents of coastal areas and on the poor in mega-cities. We can also expect to see a new category of refugees - 'environmental refugees'.

On a more global scale, the world's forests are disappearing at a rate of 15 million hectares each year, with most of the losses occurring in humid parts of all regions. With the present rate of deforestation, about 40% of the remaining forest cover in all developing countries may be lost by the year 2000. Two fifths of Africa's non-desert land risks being turned into deserts, as does one third of that in Asia and one fifth of that in Latin America. Already, acid precipitation and other forms of industrial air pollution have damaged more than 12 thousand square miles, one fifth of the total temperate forested areas in Europe. The rapid destruction of tropical rain forests does not occur only because of the survival needs of poor people living nearby, but also because of increasing demand patterns of industrialised countries. Importing industrialised countries are consuming tropical hardwoods at a rate fifteen times their 1950 level. This is contrasted with producing countries which have increased their consumption by only three times their previous levels. The over cutting of forests also causes the loss of numerous species and genetic resources, as well as increases in soil erosion and downstream flooding. It is estimated that over the next twenty-five years, at least two million species will be in danger of extinction.

The longer these circumstances persist, the higher the risks and remedial costs will be as well as the impact on the economic and social life of billions of people.

The social and economic costs of environmental degradation are very heavy - but normally not reflected in national income accounts. For instance, in Germany the cost of damage caused by transport noise is nearly 2% of GNP. In Costa Rica, the accumulated depreciation of its forests, soils and livestock amount to more than $4.6 billion (in 1989 dollars) between 1970 and 1990 - about 6% of its total GDP in that period. In Indonesia, the accumulated depreciation of forests, soils and fisheries between 1971 and 1984 amounted to $96 billion (in 1989 dollars) - about 9% of its GDP in that period.

It would be a mistake to assume that the perceptions of environmental problems, their origins and their impact on development are identical for the industrial countries of the North and for the developing countries of the South.

The environmental problems of the North are the result of over-development, extravagant consumption of fossil fuels and unrestrained demands for ever larger quantities of goods and services.

Environmental degradation in the developing countries of the South is regarded frequently as a symptom, or an end product, of poverty. A rapidly growing population puts pressure on the natural resources of a country. The increasing demands for food and basic energy needs for cooking and heating result in the destruction of forests, degradation of the soil and the depletion of water supplies. Most of the sub-Saharan African countries can be cited as prime examples of this phenomenon. These countries are deficient mostly in usable energy resources. In addition to climatic changes and soil desertification, the crash in world prices of agricultural commodities is robbing most of the farmers of the South of their jobs. They do not benefit from governmental subsidies, regulations and social security. Similarly, new discoveries in biotechnology are drastically changing the form of agricultural production. The farmers of the South neither possess, nor are knowledgeable of such technologies. They often have no other choice but to exploit the natural resources to which they have access in order to meet their daily survival and energy needs. The end result - poverty - becomes the major source of physical environmental deterioration and ecological depletion.

In looking at environmental problems of industrial countries, there too, short-term measures are adopted at the expense of long-term measures and local concerns take precedence over global issues. The end result is that insufficient action is taken all round.

The underlying question is to what extent the industrialised world is willing to undertake major lifestyle changes in order to cope with global environmental problems and ensure a more sustainable pattern of development. In considering this issue, three distinct characteristics present themselves.

First, environment and development are among those very rare subjects on which there is consensus among both industrialised and developing countries: all agree that some global action and co-operation is required. Concrete proof of this is 'Agenda 21', adopted by the Earth Summit - the United Nations Conference on Environment and Development, which took place in Rio de Janeiro, Brazil, in 1992.

The second, distinct characteristic of the recent re-emergence of environmental concerns, is the end product of strong lobbying efforts on the part of non-governmental organisations, constituencies of national conservationists, media networks and international think-tanks and not the result of governmental foresight and leadership. These are the movements which revived the environmental concerns of the early 1970s, influenced governments to embark upon a new joint undertaking and generated the present growing awareness that higher growth and eradication of poverty are equally essential to the preservation of the environment.

Thirdly, the emerging conception that environment and development are very closely linked shows that the world is increasingly confronted with issues that affect people as a whole.

In developing institutional responsibility and capacity at the national, regional and international levels to deal with issues of environment and development, consideration needs to be given to the following:

• Ecological and developmental issues cannot be solved by fragmented sectoral or national approaches alone. Their solutions require multi-disciplinary joint undertakings. Environmental damage can no longer be corrected solely by the operations of market forces; therefore, the intervention of public action becomes essential. A choice cannot be made between economic growth and environmental protection. Growth is an imperative. The issue is not *how much* economic growth, but *what kind* of growth. It is the composition of GDP - the product mix as well as the types of production processes - that alone can tell us whether the overall impact on the environment is positive or negative.

• For industrial countries also, stoppage of growth or even a serious slow down is not much of an option. Slower growth in the developed countries will imperil growth rates in poor nations. Continued growth in the industrial nations is necessary to generate both the new environmentally-safe technologies and extra financial resources for transfer to developing countries. However, the current emphasis on quantitative growth should be replaced by more concern with qualitative growth.

• The new models of sustainable human development must place 'people' at the very centre of their concern. Environmental protection is vital, but like economic growth, it is merely a means. The primary objective of our efforts must be to protect human life, develop human skills, ensure the release of human energy and provide opportunities for people to make maximum contributions to their own and societal development. These new models must also be based on the adoption of environmentally-sound technologies. This is particularly important in the energy sector.

• Strong incentives must be provided for reflecting the correct value of the environment in decision-making processes. Markets and private investors often regard environment as a free resource. We must avoid equating 'growth of consumption' with 'economic progress'.

• The true costs of production need to be accounted for. Changes must be made in the ways in which nations account for their GNP. This conventional yardstick of growth does not take into account the gain or loss of national resources, environmental enhancement or degradation. This applies also to the developing countries. Environmental degradation must be factored into the total costs of production.

• Every investment decision has environmental effects that may extend beyond local and national borders. Successful and effective results can be achieved only if the business community is challenged to be involved constructively in defining environmental problems and developing solutions.

• Sustainable human development models must be participatory and community based. All sectors of the civil society have something valuable to contribute.

In the face of threats of an irreversible nature, a comprehensive agenda for action needs to be fully implemented at all levels to prevent further degradation of the global environment and the earth's ecosystems. We have to develop new partnerships among governments, scientific communities, industry, the media, non-governmental organisations and grassroots movements to this effect. All countries must take effective action, both separately and jointly, for the protection and enhancement of environmental security, as well as economic prosperity.

Both industrialised and developing countries need to integrate environmental and ecological dimensions in their economic, human, and social planning and policies. The degradation of ecological balances and the loss of biological diversity require concrete policy actions and co-ordination at the local, national, regional and international levels. Meeting the short-term development needs of today should not impair the long-term prospects of future generations' human development.

We can no longer operate through systems which our shrinking planet has rendered obsolete. The central concept of the relationship between nations must be co-operation, interaction and partnership. Humanity is a part of the complex planetary system. We must learn to live with a global perspective.

On the eve of a new millennium, the international community has both the ability and the chance to change the many threats of today to opportunity for human progress tomorrow. However, it needs new vision, long-term perspectives and bold leadership to succeed. If we do not think of the future, we cannot have one.

The Living Resources

Jane Lubchenco

The plants, animals and microbes of the oceans are rich beyond imagining. Life below the surface is wondrously diverse, exotic and marvellous. It used to be thought that the seas were so vast that little could affect them. The phrase 'dilution is the solution to pollution' captures the old general attitudes toward most activities affecting the oceans. The oceans are vast, bountiful and infinitely resilient - or so we thought.

A series of recent events has revealed how misplaced these attitudes are. We are learning that the oceans, especially coastal areas, are under increasing and serious threat from multiple sources. We do not yet know the full extent of the problems, but marine scientists are in strong agreement that we are faced with a crisis of unprecedented complexity, proportions and consequences.

We have witnessed multiple *symptoms* which reflect numerous problems. We know there are a number of activities which pose *threats* to life in the seas. We are beginning to discover the *consequences* of some of these activities and the *challenges* in dealing with them. Let me take each of these in turn: symptoms, threats, consequences and challenges.

Symptoms

There are clear signals that we are faced with multiple problems, the most serious of which are as follows.

1. The seventeen major oceanic fisheries are all now being fished at or beyond capacity and nine of them are in a state of decline. The world-wide seafood production per person from 1950 to 1988 increased by 128% but from 1988 to 1993 decreased by 9%.

2. Non-commercial gleaning of seaweeds, shellfish and fish from local shores, which provides a significant amount of the nutrition of many peoples around the world, is also declining precipitously.

3. Unexpected, dramatic mass mortalities of many marine species are reported: marine mammal die-offs, fish kills, mass mortality of sea urchins, abalone, seagrasses and others.

4. The incidence of coral reef bleaching appears to be increasing.

5. Water quality in coastal regions is seriously impaired and in many places represents a critical human health hazard.

6. Increases in litter and trash, especially plastics, are obvious to almost everyone.

7. There appears to be an increase in blooms of toxic algae, such as those producing red tides, specifically increases in the magnitude, frequency and extent of these blooms. The consequences range from human health hazards such as paralytic shellfish poisoning, to aquacultural die-offs, to increased mortality of fishes and marine mammals.

These symptoms vary considerably in space and time; some are well documented; others less so. The symptoms are of obvious concern. Most of the world's population lives within 80 km of the coast. Coral reefs, estuaries, kelp forests and rocky shores are among the most productive ecosystems on Earth. Coastal fisheries are the richest in the world, with 75% of the world's fish catch coming from coastal waters.

Both land-based and ocean-based activities are concentrated at the coastal margins: tourism, recreation, fishing, mariculture, domestic and industrial waste disposal, military activities, transportation, mining and energy industries. This plethora of *activities*, the increasing *migration* of people around the world to coastal regions, the explosive *growth* of the human population and the *overconsumption* of resources are causing the changes we see reflected in the symptoms.

Threats

A number of recent scientific assessments list the following most important agents of present and potential change. (The order does not imply relative importance.)

1. Fisheries operations.

2. Chemical pollution.

3. Eutrophication.

4. Alteration of physical habitats (e.g. from trampling, trawling, dredging, drilling, dynamiting, building and dumping).

5. Invasion of exotic species.

6. Global climatic change.

7. Increases in UV-B radiation as a result of stratospheric ozone depletion.

Of these threats, pollution and climatic change have received much attention. There is no doubt that both of these are of critical importance. At the same time, over-fishing, habitat destruction and introduced species are in some places more serious or more immediate problems.

The magnitude of the problem of introduced species has only recently become known.

Some species are transported around the globe in the ballast water of ships. It has been estimated that more than 3000 species a day are in motion inside the giant aquaria that serve as ballast tanks in ocean-going vessels. These introduced species have the potential to completely alter the trophic structure and ecosystem dynamics of bays and estuaries into which ballast water is discharged.

The loss of biological diversity resulting from habitat destruction and introduced species is of particular concern because it is irreversible and because people are so dependent upon the living resources of the ocean.

Consequences

I have described seven major symptoms and seven major threats. What are the likely consequences of these problems?

Marine life has already been altered to a large extent, sometimes with dramatic consequences.

In considering consequences, we tend to focus primarily on alterations to the *goods* which we reap from the oceans. Changes in the *ecological services* provided by ecosystems are also of great importance. Let me explain.

Ecological systems provide *goods* such as food, fibre, fuel, medicines, chemicals and genes which people use or trade. Ecological systems also provide *services,* for example:

• kelp forests and estuaries provide habitats and nursery areas for many economically important fishes;

• oysters filter and cleanse the water of bays and estuaries;

• kelp forests, mangroves and coral reefs protect coastal shores from erosion during storms;

• some phytoplankton may play a key role in regulating climate.

These ecological services, also called ecosystem services, are provided free of charge. They are largely outside our systems of economic valuation. They are of critical importance to us, but are largely unappreciated.

A recently completed international scientific assessment called the Global Biodiversity Assessment sponsored by the United Nations Environment Programme and published by Cambridge University Press (1995) draws attention to the links between biodiversity and the continued provision of these ecosystem services. This is an exciting new area of research with much promise for providing useful information for policy and management.

The suite of activities mentioned earlier is threatening both the ecological goods and the ecological services of the seas. Even fisheries that were once thought to be inexhaustible, for example on the Georges Banks or the Grand Banks, are collapsing. Oyster populations in Chesapeake Bay that once filtered the entire Chesapeake estuary once a week now filter it only once a year. Stock depletion from over-fishing and disease have taken their toll not only on the food provided by oysters but also on the services of water filtration and cleansing which they provide.

Challenges

In the light of these consequences, what are the challenges?

The changes we are precipitating are unprecedented in their magnitude, kind and rate. Making predictions about likely outcomes of different possible management or policy options is extremely difficult. This uncertainty, coupled with incomplete baseline information about many systems presents enormous challenges. I echo and emphasise Professor Norman Myers' points made in his paper about the future holding surprises and uncertainty. This uncertainty and the likely irreversible consequences of many paths should make us much more careful and cautious.

The best possible scientific information should be readily available and easily understood by a wide variety of possible users. In some cases, we have insufficient scientific information to make informed decisions. Research to obtain urgently needed information is appropriate. In many other cases, sufficient information exists but is not communicated adequately or is not used. New mechanisms are needed to disseminate scientific information more efficiently and effectively and to utilise it more appropriately.

It would be useful to have a comprehensive, international scientific assessment of the state of the world's oceans. Such an assessment could be quite useful in providing a consensus statement on which to ground discussions about the wide variety of topics considered above. We might even be so bold as to suggest it be named OIKOS for Our International Knowledge of the Ocean State ('o*ikos*' of course being the Greek root for our words 'ecology' and 'economics').

Conclusions

I have tried to summarise some of the symptoms, threats, consequences and challenges concerning the living resources of the seas. I was asked to address the question: 'What is at stake?' My answer is, very simply, 'Our future, and that of our children and grandchildren.' Why? Because a sustainable biosphere requires a living ocean. Moreover, it is clear to me that the seas are loved by many, needed by all but cared for by none.

Thus far we have failed to be good stewards of the oceans. Based on the knowledge summarised above, we have an urgent responsibility to work together to be better stewards, in short, to act.

Chapter 3

Improving the state of our knowledge

Introduction

Jane Lubchenco

In this chapter, we explore the status of water and how it is held in the consciousness of different traditions as a body of knowledge that can be drawn on when seeking solutions to environmental destruction.

Vaasiliifiti Moelagi Jackson describes the importance of water to her community in the Pacific and the threat from nuclear testing. In her culture, water is life, it cleanses the spirit and gives blessing and is to be guarded with one's life. The mystical significance of water to the Orthodox Church and its capacity to save the individual through baptism is described by Ioannis Fountoulis. 'In the sanctifying actions of the Church involving water...the work of divine creation is repeated and renewed.'

The possibility of renewal is a theme taken up by Norman Myers, whose view is that we live in momentous times with profound problems that can still be turned into splendid opportunities. 'If we switch from breakdown to breakthrough, we shall be acclaimed way beyond the year 2010. We are the sole generation to face such an extreme yet glorious prospect.'

Yet why is it, asks Herman Daly, that this message of hope is so little heard and acted upon with any sense of urgency? He argues that scientific materialism, in its renunciation of any religious interpretation of the cosmos, has denied the reality of purpose and makes it difficult to convince people that they should love this same purposeless world enough to fight to save it. It is a recognition of the purpose of Creation that needs to be recaptured.

Bo Krantz offers a down-to-earth example of how to engage and motivate the public to become involved with their environment while having fun. Established in 1991, the Stockholm Water Festival is now the second biggest event in Europe, disseminating vital information from scientific sources to the public and instilling a sense of personal responsibility for the care of water.

Spirituality, Scientific Knowledge and Environmental Concerns

Vaasiliifiti Moelagi Jackson

I come from a group of islands whose culture remains strong, guarded by the chiefs and orators, the councils of women, and the young people of our country. Before a meeting is opened, there is always a Kava Ceremony. A special powder, prepared from the root of the *methysticum* plant, is mixed with water by a female or male dignitary in front of the elders while they offer prayers of thanksgiving and pray for God's guidance in their daily and future ventures. During this ceremony the importance of water, and the love God has shown to us by the provision of it, are highlighted.

Samoa is a group of islands in the middle of the South Pacific inhabited by Polynesian people. Our total land area is just over 1,100 square miles. Water is everywhere, all around us. Although the Pacific zone is the largest zone in the world, almost 80% is comprised of water.

In our culture water is life - and it is guarded with one's life. Water cleanses the spirit and gives blessing and favour to a completed work. A new canoe may have a short life if the owner fails to dip the entire canoe into the water and dry it properly before it is put into use. To dip a newly completed piece of work often calls for special ceremonies and celebrations.

For us water is a sign of joy and celebration. In the United States parents take their children to Disneyland to celebrate. In Samoa it is a treat to take one's children for a swim in the pools or the sea. The feeling of being enveloped by water is refreshing and satisfying. We refer to it as *dancing with nature*.

Most of our thinking is governed by water. We have a saying: *Moe I le vai, ae ala I le ai.* (Sleep in water and wake up to eat.) It means as long as you get water you can sleep without food until you awaken. Another saying, *E inu I Malie ae ou te le malie,* (I drink at the village of Malie, though my thirst is not quenched) means, I have drunk but will be thirsty for more again. It is a warning of the value of water even after you have taken enough for the present time.

Back home there is a hill top village called Aopo that is located on newly formed lava. The lava is so porous that it cannot hold water. The people of Aopo must travel for miles to get drinking water. When travelling to this village, it is best to carry a container of water with you. It is because of this that when the going is hard or our people cannot come to a decision, someone will be heard to say, *Ua tali I lagi le vai o Aopo.* (Let us be like the people of Aopo, who wait for water from Heaven.) This means: God alone will give us a decision so let us stop worrying over it and pray. Aopo can only get water when it rains, and the rains do not come often due to the village's location on the mountain. When it does come, it comes from Heaven.

I know that for people from countries with large landmasses it may be difficult to understand how we of the Pacific Islands are bound in heart and spirit to the water. I was born and brought up on a beach where I awakened to hear the waves. As a child I ran to the beach to write and draw pictures in the sand, or throw pebbles at the waves and count how many times they skipped on the water. Often I ended up in the water myself.

I was lucky to be born in a village where there was a river nearby. The sea and that river became my very close friends. It was exciting to go walking on the reef at low tide looking for shellfish and the many edible weeds, and collecting shells to make my own necklaces or containers and tools to use at home. The sea around us is so rich and accessible as a place to find food, to have fun or to paddle across in a canoe.

Water is also often used by our people for spiritual healing. Our traditional herbal healers believe that they can communicate with the Spirit that gives them their healing power through water perfumed with flowers and leaves from the forest.

This is why we are so hurt and disturbed by the French nuclear testing in the Pacific. It has the power to completely subvert our lives and our livelihood. I have four girls, all of whom love the sea just as I did as a child. Can you imagine Island parents having to protect their children from contaminated water in the sea when something goes wrong with these nuclear tests? The sea which they love and which gives them life? All of the Pacific peoples are protesting about the French nuclear testing at Mururoa atoll because the ocean of Mururoa is our beloved Pacific. It is our *food*, it is our *life*, it is our *everything*. We protect our land and our rainforest because they hold water. If there is no water there will be no forest and, of course, there will be no life. We *must* guard our Pacific.

Many islands in the Pacific are not so blessed with water as we are, even though water surrounds them. Pacific Islanders attach great importance to good, clean water and look on it as a blessing. Historically, Islanders have travelled the Pacific Ocean sailing from island to island looking for sweet, clean water as medicine for their kings, queens, high chiefs and peoples.

Our language is full of words and expressions pertaining to water: *Vaisa* - sacred water, *Vaitele* - big water, *Vailoa* - many waters, *Vaiola* - living water, *Vailele* - flying water, *Vaipuna* - spring water, *Vaipisia* - sprinkling water and *Vaillli* - shaking water, are just a few.

Many islands, villages and people are named after water, according to our myths and legends. Here is the story of how one famous place got its name.

One day an old woman and a child were crossing the island. The day was hot, which made the trip a hard one for the two. As they were descending a mountain toward the lowland, the old woman could hardly walk, partly from tiredness but more especially from thirst. The child, having realised her situation, immediately dashed around the bush and jungle listening for the sound of water. Soon she found water but could not find a container to fetch it. She went back to the old woman and reported the problem. The old woman opened her eyes at the mention of water. Though she could not move, she replied to the child, *'Ta fia inu I se vai o ou lima.'* (I wish I could drink from your hands.) The child ran back and in the palms of her hands she carried water until the old woman had had enough to drink. The old woman blessed the child and said, 'This spot will be called *Vailima* (water in the hands) to mark how you saved me with the water from your hands'.

This is the same spot on which Robert Louis Stevenson, the Scottish author, chose to build his home many years ago. His home at Vailima Village was turned into a Western Samoan Museum in 1994 to commemorate the 100th anniversary of his death in Samoa. His fame as a writer has helped make Vailima a famous name. The name is also used for trade and water products such as our Vailima beer. The name Vailima, whenever it is mentioned, always reminds us of the importance of the water that revived the old woman, and saved her life.

Samoans and the Pacific islanders have many ceremonies and stories involving water as the source of life that are paralleled in the Bible.

• Our Kava Ceremony is similar to communion. Before a chief drinks his kava he says a little prayer as happens in communion ceremonies.

• The dipping of new work and the bathing of a healed person with scented water reminds us of Jesus' baptism.

• We have many stories in which people have been revived from death through water. As a Christian, I see these as parallels of Jesus' death on the cross and Resurrection.

In Genesis 2:5-15, when God made the heavens and the earth there was no growth until rain was finally created. It was the four rivers that produced life in the Garden of Eden. In the Book of Ezekiel 47: 1-15 the focus is on how water flowed from under the temple near the altar out to the land and to the sea. Wherever the water flowed, there was growth. This emphasises the integration of water from the land with that of the sea and how marine life enriched the land with plants for food and healing. In the Book of Revelation, chapter 22 is a parallel of the scene in Genesis with the four rivers. In all three of these examples there is an emphasis on water as the source of life.

I believe that water is, for the Pacific, a heritage from God and our only means of survival. Our resources and lives are locked into the availability of good, clean water, therefore we must do everything possible to protect and guard it. We are not a strong region physically and economically, but spiritually we *are* strong! We are praying that God will help us and that, in due course, Chirac's decision will be reversed so that our peaceful Pacific will remain safe for us and our children and for others when they come to visit us.

The Significance of Water: a Mystical Interpretation

Ioannis M Fountoulis

The theological conception of the Orthodox Church is the basis of this brief exposition on the mystical significance of water. It is expressed in various liturgical texts, in prayers, hymns and sacred rituals, where water is given a prominent place, interpreted as a symbol, or is seen as serving the divine work of salvation.

In particular, wonderful poetic comments are found in the hymnody inspired by the first and sixth biblical canticles, in the corresponding *heirmos* of the *Kanons*. The first canticle is the hymn following the wondrous crossing of the Red Sea by the Jewish people during the exodus from Egypt ('I will sing unto the Lord, for he hath triumphed gloriously: the horse and his rider hath he thrown into the sea ...' Exodus 15:1) and the sixth is the canticle of the prophet Jonah in the fish's belly ('I cried by reason of my affliction unto the Lord ...' Jonah 2:1-10).

The mid-Pentecost, one of the feasts of the liturgical year, has as its theme the teachings of Christ about the 'living water' (John 5:14-30) and comes between two Sundays in which the readings from the New Testament and the hymnody relate to events which are connected with water, that is, the healing of the paralytic in the pool of Bethseda (John 5:1-15) and the dialogue of the Lord with the Samaritan woman by Jacob's well (John 4:5-13).

Two services involve the blessing of the waters: the great benediction of Epiphany and the so-called 'lesser blessing'. The climax of the Church's theology regarding water comes with the feast of Epiphany - the occasion of the Lord's baptism - and in the service of the holy baptism of the faithful.

It is significant that the grandiose description of Creation in the first chapter of Genesis is the first reading during the vespers of the three great 'cosmogonic' feasts of the liturgical year, the three great baptismal days - Christmas, Epiphany and Easter: the Spirit of God 'moved upon the face of the waters' and His word divided the waters which were 'under the firmament' from the waters which were 'above the firmament'. It was He who gathered 'the waters under the heaven ... together in one place', the sea, and let 'the dry land appear' (Genesis 1:1-10).

Pursuing the study of biblical references to water, one notes an antithetical juxtaposition between two symbols: the waters are divided into the 'bitter water' that is the sea, and the 'sweet' water, that of springs and rivers. Already in Genesis we find this antithesis indirectly suggested. The sea waters, at the command of God, draw back 'unto one place' in order to give space to dry land, for grasses and herbs to grow, and for the living creatures of the land to survive. They remain on the outer limits of the world, with some sort of latent tendency to regain their initial cosmic dominance. The power of God's word, however, holds them back in their predetermined space, since, by God's will, 'the formerly freely-flowing nature of the waters took the form of its earthly counterpart ... the fluid nature of the waters, shrinking, was compressed unto itself' (*Heirmos*, first ode). In the Psalms (104:9) and in the Book of Job (38:8-11) there is a personification of the sea and a dramatic description of God's creative intervention of the third day of Creation. Psalm 107 gives a truly wonderful description of the fear of those caught in a tempest and of their strong faith and hope, nevertheless, in God's stilling of the storm.

These are just about the only descriptions of the sea and of its world. Its beauty, its marvellous shores, its ecological importance, its role in facilitating communication between peoples, are all absent. This is exactly the viewpoint from which inland peoples - the ancient tribe of Israel - regard the sea, and which influences their liturgical conception of it.

The sea is not, of course, a power opposed to the divine, a demonic element alien to God; for it, too, is 'very good', as are all things made by God (Genesis 1:31). In the main, however, the symbol of the sea is utilised to define negative states: we have the 'saltiness' of secular unbelief, the 'deepest abyss' of sin and the insolence of the impious ('Raging waves of the sea, foaming out of their own shame' Jude 13).

The references to the sea found in the Book of Revelation seem to suggest that the negative elements have been somewhat toned down. There appears to be a familiarisation with the mysterious world of the sea, with the prophet standing 'upon the sand of the sea', 'in the isle that is called Patmos' (Revelation 13:1, 1:9). There is also the open space before the throne of God, which is described as a 'sea of glass like unto crystal' (Revelation 4:6); and in heaven 'a sea of glass mingled with fire' (Revelation 15:1-4).

However, it is from the sea that the seven-horned beast emerges (Revelation 13:1), as the prophet Daniel had earlier seen in a vision (Daniel 7), and it is on 'many waters' that the whore, 'great Babylon' (Revelation 16:19, 17:1ff, 18:1ff) sits, again in accord with the prophetic prototypes of the Old Testament. This is why it is not surprising that in the new heaven and in the new earth the sea will no longer exist: '... and there was no more sea ... for the first heaven and the first earth were passed away' (Revelation 21:1-4). The polyvalent symbol of the sea no longer has a reason for existence in the new world, in the Kingdom of God.

Contrarily, in the final vision of the Revelation, John sees 'a pure river of water of life, clear as crystal, proceeding out of the throne of God and of the Lamb. In the midst of the street of it, and on either side of the river, was there the tree of life' (Revelation

22:1-2). This image clearly corresponds to that found in the garden of Eden: 'a river went out of Eden to water the garden; and from thence it was parted, and became into four heads (the rivers Pison, Gihon, Tigris and Euphrates) ...' and there was 'the tree of life also in the midst of the garden' (Genesis 2:8ff). And in the prophet Ezekiel's vision of the sanctuary of God (chapter 47), a river of waters issues from the house. The waters of springs and rivers provide an image of life to peoples such as Israel, in whom the memory of their lengthy sojourn in 'a dry and thirsty land' (Psalm 62:2) remained vivid. The symbol is easily spiritualised. God, the provider of material water in this world, is compared to the source of life, to the living water, which both gives life and washes away the sins of man. In this last sense, St. John the Baptist calls the people to a 'baptism of repentance for the remission of sins' (Mark 1:4). The waters of the river Jordan which baptise Christ are transformed into 'healers' of human nature through the presence in them of the Holy Spirit. The voice of the Father, bearing witness to His kinship with Christ, His own Son by nature, confirms His adoption of the baptised by grace. Thenceforward baptism in the name of the Father and of the Son and of the Holy Spirit is not only a 'baptism of repentance for the remission of sins', but a 'washing of regeneration, and renewing of the Holy Ghost' (Titus 3:5), a new birth in God. By invoking the terrible name of God, in the exorcisms of the waters of the baptismal font, the evil forces lurking in these waters since man's rebellion are destroyed, and the baptised person returns to his original, natural state of purity, as in God's original creative will.

By extension, through the invocation of the Holy Spirit, in the rite we know as *hagiasmos*, the waters become the purveyors of divine graces, when they are drunk or sprinkled 'for the health of body and soul'; they also ward off evil forces and sanctify all objects in creation.

In the sanctifying actions of the Church involving water and in the theological teachings expressed therein, the work of divine creation is repeated and renewed, 'the Spirit of God' once again 'moving upon the face of the waters' (Genesis 1:2), and the people of God enjoying in advance the eschatological promise of God in the Revelation: 'I will give unto him that is athirst of the fountain of the water of life freely ... and I will be his God, and he shall be my son' (Revelation 21:6-7).

And what of the sea? What the official church liturgy did not foresee, in accordance with the landlocked archaic Jewish tradition, was dared by the people of the islands and the coasts, in their popular devotion and piety: they immerse the Cross of the Lord into the sea on the day of the feast of the Holy Epiphany, the day of 'Lights', in imitation of the Lord's baptism, for the blessing of the waters of the sea.

Thus is fulfilled the word of the holy hymnographer: 'Today the nature of the waters is made holy' (hymnos on the feast of Epiphany) and the blessing of Epiphany comes to pass:

> Earth and sea partake of the joy of the world: and the world is filled with gladness.

An Age of Environmental Opportunity

*Norman Myers**

We live in momentous times concerning our environmental prospect. They are times of profound problems that can still be turned into splendid opportunities.

There is no doubt about the gravity of our environmental prospect. During the course of 1992, two scientific bodies issued statements to review our bleak outlook, arguing that we should pull the levers of corrective decision with all urgency. The Royal Society of London and the US National Academy of Science jointly stated that, 'Environmental changes may produce irreversible damage to the Earth's capacity to sustain life. The future of our planet is in the balance.' Similarly, the Union of Concerned Scientists issued a declaration signed by 1,680 scientific leaders in 70 countries, including 104 Nobel Laureates, to the effect that, 'We are fast approaching many of the Earth's limits. No more than one or a few decades remain before the chance to avert environmental threats will be lost and the prospect for humanity immeasurably diminished.'

These two statements effectively endorsed a consensus agreed by 130 Prime Ministers, Presidents and other Heads of State at the Rio Earth Summit in June 1992. This was far and away the largest number of political leaders ever to forgather. Like scientists, politicians tend to be cold-eyed people, not given to 'way out' assertions. Unlike scientists, some of them are so ecologically illiterate they would suppose a food chain to be a line of supermarkets. Yet the Rio gathering supported a statement to the effect that the threat of global environmental ruin is surpassed only by the threat of nuclear war. The politicians might have added that whereas we could restore most of the damage of a nuclear war within half a century, many of our environmental assaults will leave the biosphere impoverished for many centuries, if not longer.

True, most of our environmental destruction could be fixed up eventually. We could clean up acid rain, push back the deserts, replant the forests, restore the topsoil, allow the ozone layer to recover, and even enable the greenhouse-affected world to regain its climatic equilibrium. But one particular item is different. Species extinction is irreversible. And we face the prospect of eliminating species in their millions, perhaps half of all that share this planet with us, by virtue of what we do (and don't do) during the immediate future. Of course, evolution will still generate new species. But so far as

---

* This paper was first printed in *The Environmentalist*, Volume 14, Number 2, 85-86 (1994) as a Guest Editorial. It is based upon an address to environmental graduates at Farnborough College of Technology, Hampshire, UK, which was delivered on 9th December 1993.

we can tell from recovery periods following mass extinctions of the prehistoric past, the length of time it will take for evolution to produce a replacement stock of species with abundance and diversity to match today's will be five million years, and possibly several times longer.

Suppose it is only five million years. This will be twenty times longer than the modern human has been a species itself. Suppose too that a human generation lasts 25 years, and that the average number of people the Earth can sustainably support is 2.5 billion people (less than half as many as today). That means that our present activities will exert their impoverishing impact on 500 trillion* people during those five million years. It is far and away the biggest decision ever made by one society on the unconsulted behalf of future society during the entire course of human history.

If our environment prospect is so dire, why don't we do something about it? It's largely a question of perception. Yesterday the world lost 65 million tonnes of topsoil (conceivably three times as much), or enough in principle to grow food to make up the diets of 600,000 semi-starving people. Yet if a farm in East Anglia is losing eight tonnes per acre a year (20t ha^{-1} yr^{-1}), this amounts to a mere one tenth of an inch (2.5mm) of surface soil. If we lost 100 species yesterday, and the sun still came up on time this morning how could we tell that it matters? When we went out of the door this morning, we were stepping into an atmosphere that is probably undergoing greater change than at any time during the past 50,000 years. Yet we can't see these changes, we can't smell or taste them. It is hard to sense the environmental ruin going on all around us.

If environmental problems struck us like a heart attack, we would rush our ecosystems to the intensive care unit and get them fixed. But environmental problems are like a cancer, working away silently and insidiously below the surface until by the time they reveal themselves it is often too late to do much about them except at vast cost and with limited hope of success.

All in all, our environmental predicament is like an experiment that school children conducted with a frog. They took the frog and dropped it into a saucepanful of boiling

---

* The number 'trillion' is much bandied about by economists, politicians and others. How far do we realise what the statistic means? How can we wrap our minds around such an immense number? Reader, try a thought experiment: Make a guesstimate of how long a period is represented by one trillion seconds. Do it quickly, don't calculate. If you claim a basic understanding of the world you live in, you should be roughly on target. Then check with your calculator. When this experiment was tried on a gathering of hot-shot scientists in Geneva a while ago, most of them were out by an order of magnitude - this writer by twice as much.

water. The frog reacted to this instantly hostile environment by skipping out. It was a bit scalded, but it was okay, it survived. The children then took the same frog and dropped it into another saucepan on the stove and turned the heat up. The frog swam around and around thinking, 'This is a fine environment, this is what I am accustomed to.' The water grew a little warmer and the frog thought, 'Better still, what an improvement.' The water got warmer again: 'Things are better by the minute.' The water grew still hotter - whereupon the frog became so drowsy that it fell into a coma and boiled to death. The world outside the window is our saucepan heating up. Can we do better than the frog?

We can do remarkable things. Think of the past few years. People have torn down the Berlin Wall, they have put an end to Communism, the Soviet Union and the Cold War. They have started talking to each other in South Africa and the Middle East, even in Bosnia and Northern Ireland. It is astonishing what people can achieve when once they set their minds to it. What is needed on the environmental front is to eliminate the Berlin Wall of ignorance and indifference in people's minds.

Time is of the super-essence. Suppose we allow ourselves until, say, the year 2010 to take the vital decisions that will affect our planetary home for hundreds, thousands and even millions of years. After the year 2010, the processes of environmental destruction will surely have worked up so much momentum that they will be hard to slow down, let alone halt or even turn around.

Till 2010 there are roughly 5,000 days. We lose one percent of our manoeuvring room every seven weeks. Exciting times to be alive!

If we switch from breakdown to breakthrough, we shall be acclaimed way beyond the year 2010. People will look back and say, 'Those people of the 1990s, when they realised what was going on, how they got to grips with the greatest challenge in history - and didn't they make themselves giants of the human condition, they must have felt ten feet tall.' We live in much more than exciting times.

I am sometimes asked if I am hopeful about our environmental outlook. There are occasions, I admit, when I am reminded of the person defining an optimist and a pessimist. The optimist proclaims that this is the best of all possible worlds - to which the pessimist responds that that is probably true. But then I snap out of my downside mood by thinking that I am a member of what is truly a privileged generation. No other human generation could enjoy a challenge so creative as ours. We have it in our hands to save our one Earth at a time when much of it is on the brink of terminal threat. And - here's the clincher - we are the sole generation to face such an extreme, yet glorious, prospect. People in the past have never enjoyed our chance since today's problems have simply never arisen before. Nor will any generation of the future have our chance, because if we do not get on with the job, our descendants will be left with nothing to do except pick up the pieces.

It is up to us alone. Shall we not count ourselves lucky to be alive at a time of unprecedented challenge? Are we not fortunate beyond dreams to be scientists, conservationists and citizens of embattled Earth at this momentous stage in the human enterprise?

Science, Religion and Sustainable Development

Herman E Daly

The environment and the economy are in mortal combat. Sustainable development is an effort to resolve this conflict. But why does the effort to deal with this impending Armageddon inspire such a low sense of urgency in major institutions like the University, the Church and most national governments? These institutions are certainly not protecting the earth from destruction in the manner of the four angels in Revelation 7:1 'holding back the four winds of the earth so that no wind could blow on land or sea or against any tree'. Of course there are individual exceptions in each of these domains - prophetic voices that cry in the wilderness. But why are these cries evoking so little response in so much wilderness?

If the Apocalypse of St John the Divine is thought simply to provide environmentalists with an ancient model for how to scare people into repentance with forecasts of doom, its message may actually be contrary to environmentalism according to former US Secretary of the Interior, James Watt. His argument was that if the end of the world is near, then it makes no sense to save anything for a non-existent beneficiary. Is there not a more hopeful message in Revelation? I believe there is, and I want to consider in some detail why this message of hope is so little heard today, why our ears have become deaf to it.

Some prominent scientists have decided that science has the techniques but is unable to ignite sufficient moral fervour to induce the public to finance the policies that apply them. They thought that it would be worth a try to appeal to religion to supply the missing moral fervour as a basis for consensus and action. This resulted, in May 1992, in the 'Joint Appeal by Science and Religion on the Environment', led by the eminent scientists Carl Sagan, Edward O. Wilson and Stephen Jay Gould, along with a few religious leaders and hosted by then Senator Al Gore. The three scientists are well known not only for their highly informed and genuine concern about the environment, but also for their scientific materialism and consequent renunciation of any religious interpretation of the cosmos. What then was their rationale for courting the religious community? It was that while science presumably had the understanding on which to act, it lacked the moral inspiration to do so and inspire others to.

I attended the conference and was vaguely troubled at the time by what seemed to me a somewhat less than honest appeal by the scientists to a rather credulous group of religious leaders. A year or so later I read a book by a theologian, John F Haught, who had also been present, and discovered that he had precisely articulated my doubts.

Haught wondered:

> whether it is completely honest for them (the scientists) to drink in this case so lustily from the stream of moral fervor that flows from what they have consistently taken to be the inappropriate and even false consciousness of religious believers... the well-intended effort by the skeptics to co-opt the moral enthusiasm of the religious for the sake of ecology is especially puzzling, in view of the fact that it is only because believers take their religious symbols and ideas to be disclosive of the *truth* of reality that they are aroused to moral passion in the first place. If devotees thought that their religions were *not* representative of the way things *really* are, then the religions would be ethically impotent'.[1]

Haught instead holds that only an integrally religious perspective is adequate:

> It is hard to imagine how any thorough transformation of the habits of humans will occur without a corporate human confidence in the ultimate worthwhileness of our moral endeavours. And without a deep trust in reality itself, ecological morality will, I am afraid, ultimately languish and die. Such trust ... must be grounded in a conviction that the universe carries a meaning, or that it is the unfolding of a 'promise'. A commonly held sense that the cosmos is a significant process, that it unfolds something analogous to what we humans call 'purpose' is, I think, an essential prerequisite of sustained global and intergenerational commitment to the earth's well-being.[2]

The point, of course, is that Sagan, Wilson and Gould proclaim the cosmology of scientific materialism, which considers the cosmos and life to be no more than accidents, ultimately reducible to dead matter in motion. In their view there is no such thing as value in any objective sense, or purpose, beyond short term survival and reproduction which are purely instinctual, and thus ultimately mechanical. Calling for a moral compass in such a world is as absurd as calling for a magnetic compass in a world in which you proclaim that there is no such thing as magnetic north.

One might reply that objective value may not exist externally, but nevertheless does exist as an internal affair created by humans (or by God in humans) and imposed by them on the external world. This is the solution of dualism, dominant since Descartes. Such a view, however, is contrary to the evolutionary understanding according to which human beings have kinship with other forms of life, as affirmed by science. On this basis scientific materialism has denied the reality of purpose, mind and value in human beings as well as in the external world, such that they are considered mere epiphenomena, ultimately explainable in terms of underlying physical structures and motions. However another resolution that still takes science seriously, is to affirm that purpose and value is not a human monopoly, but is the basis of the real kinship among species.

This alternative to scientific materialism is worked out in the process philosophy of Alfred North Whitehead. His view is radically empirical. What we know most concretely and directly, unmediated by the sometimes deceptive senses or by abstract concepts, is our inner experience of purpose. That should be the starting point, the most well known thing in terms of which we try to explain less well known things. To begin with highly abstract concepts, such as electrons and photons, and explain the immediate experience of purpose as an 'epiphenomenon' incidentally produced by the behaviour of these abstractions, is an example of what Whitehead called the 'fallacy of misplaced concreteness'. I do not pretend that Whiteheadean philosophy is without difficulties of its own, but it strains my credulity a lot less than scientific materialism. Whitehead observed, 'Scientists animated by the purpose of proving that they are purposeless constitute an interesting subject for study'.[3]

We might add that religious persons animated by belief in a Creator God, yet happily participating in the destruction of Creation, also constitute an interesting subject for study. It is indeed a paradox that people whose professed beliefs give them no good reason to be environmentalists are usually trying harder to save the environment than are people whose beliefs give them a very good reason to be environmentalists. Gould has noted that 'we will not fight to save what we do not love'.[4] God's world *is* loveable and ironically scientists often fall in love with it much more deeply than theologians! There is something fundamentally silly about biologists teaching on MWF that everything, including our sense of value and reason, is a purposeless product of genetic chance and environmental necessity, and then on TTS trying to convince the public that they should love this same purposeless world enough to fight to save it. They are trying to live by the fruit of the tree whose tap root they are cutting. Our entire society, including the scientists, is living off the depleting moral capital of traditional religious belief, just as surely as it is living off the depleting natural capital of the ecosystem.

In the discussions during the meeting in Washington DC of the joint appeal, the void of purpose was frequently glossed over in discussions with the phrase 'for our children'. But of course if we are accidents then so are they, and the question is merely begged by pushing it one generation forward. I recall that one lady was so annoyed by this cloying invocation of 'our children', that she took the microphone to say that she had no children, so was she to understand that she had no reason to care about the future of God's Creation? Though she was not even an official participant, I thought her intervention one of the best.

Environmentalists really must face up to deep philosophical and religious questions about why their efforts ultimately make sense. Neither vague pantheistic sentimentality about Gaia, nor the *ad hoc* invention of instincts like 'biophilia' can withstand much philosophical criticism, though they are welcome first steps away from scientific materialism. I find the ideals of a minority of Christian thinkers influenced by Whitehead, such as John B Cobb, Jr, John F Haught and Charles Birch, to offer a much more solid base than either scientific materialism or traditional theology for loving nature enough to save it.

Many traditional religions also share a theology of creation (not the same as the literalistic doctrine of 'scientific creationism'), so a theological basis for 'biophilia' as a persuasive virtue rather than a mechanical instinct is by no means limited to Christianity. All traditional religions are in fact enemies of the same modern idolatry - the idea that accidental man through science and technology is the true creator, and that the natural world is just the instrument to be used in furthering the arbitrary projects of one purposeless species. If we cannot assert a more coherent cosmology than that, then we might as well close the door and all go fishing - at least, while the fish last.

I certainly sympathise with the Eastern Church's early reluctance to admit Revelation to the Canon. We no longer understand the imagery of apocalyptic literature, and consequently the book has become the happy hunting ground for crazed, literalist, would-be messiahs of which David Koresh is only the most recent. But we need its affirmation of cosmic purpose today. In fact, it is the denial of purpose, explicit in modern scientific materialism and deconstructionism, that drives people to look for purpose wherever they can find it, underground, as it were. Universities have totally abdicated on questions of meaning and purpose, while mainline Churches are often so identified with the dominant culture that their affirmation seems muted. This frequently leaves fundamentalist sects as the only alternative to secular meaninglessness.

It is the message of the purpose of Creation that must be recaptured on the nineteen-hundredth anniversary of the Book of Revelation. To claim that the whole show is a purposeless exercise in random change leaves would-be environmentalists without a leg to stand on. Both science and Christianity believe that the world will end - even Revelation's four angels at the four corners of the earth were only *temporarily* holding back the winds of destruction. However Christianity affirms God's promise that neither the world while it exists, nor its ultimate demise, are purposeless. To end the world prematurely by our own actions, I submit, is to usurp God's prerogative and is analogous to an individual committing suicide. In Revelation, after all the conflict, destruction, and decay, God's promise is affirmed in the final vision - that of the same tree of life as in Genesis, but this time instead of forbidden fruit it has healing leaves.

1 John F Haught, *The Promise of Nature: Ecology and Cosmic Purpose*, The Paulist Press: Mahwah, N J, 1993, p.9. See also Charles Birch, *On Purpose*, New South Wales University Press Ltd., Kensington, NSW, Australia, 1980.

[2] Haught, op cit. p.7

[3] A N Whitehead, *The Function of Reason*, Princeton University Press, 1929, p.16

[4] S J Gould, *Unenchanted Evening*, Natural History September 1991, p.14. For an insightful discussion see David Orr, *Earth in Mind,* Island Press, Washington DC, 1994, Chapter 20.

Utile Dulce, or How to Make it Happen

Bo Krantz

It seems to be an axiom that anything that is of importance to mankind, such as questions concerning morality, technology, the environment, religion or education, has great difficulty in winning either recognition or interest among the general public. The only exception is probably medicine, but that is not surprising since it encompasses questions of life and death and therefore has a high profile in our self interest. In contrast, anything superficial, foolish, meaningless, blasphemous or outright stupid attracts an indecent amount of public attention and often financial sacrifice.

A perfectly logical way of attracting public attention to a project of vital interest for mankind would therefore be to make it look as superficial and foolish as possible. Fortunately, superficial and foolish may sometimes be spelled *fun*.

The Stockholm Water Foundation was founded six years ago, with the sole purpose of focusing the world's attention on the troubled situation of our common resource, water. The founding fathers were the Kingdom of Sweden, the City of Stockholm and a group of industrialists, all sharing the belief that if a such project was to be successful it had to be built on public participation rather than as a large-scale bureaucratic project. The first objective was to try to define the means of communicating the message. For Swedes the solution was quite obvious - make the message look as appetising as possible.

On the scientific side of the project, this was fairly easy. Sweden has a great tradition when it comes to rewarding research and development, most commonly recognised in the Nobel Prizes. We assent to the simple idea that scientists and technicians need as much recognition as anyone else to feel motivated and perform to the best of their ability. Hence the Stockholm Water Prize was inaugurated and the first prize (to the Canadian professor David Schindler) awarded in August 1991. Since then the 150,000 US dollar prize has gone to Denmark, India, Japan and Great Britain.

How would we capture public interest? The answer was a mixture of nature, pride and guilt. Sweden in general and Stockholm in particular is blessed with an abundance of clean, fresh water, mainly because of farsighted political decisions during the 1950s. It is the unpolluted waterways of Stockholm that give our capital its image and character. Every Stockholmer loves these waterways and they are a major tourist attraction in themselves. Moreover, every Stockholmer takes great pride in them and is very inquisitive indeed when it comes to questions regarding the handling of the Stockholm waters. What about guilt? Well, we Swedes have a slight hang-up when it comes to enjoying ourselves. It seems to us much more proper to strive and work than to rest and enjoy - a very Lutheran approach.

The only thing we could think of which would combine these three elements was of course a festival - *a Water Festival.* We came up with the idea of nine days packed with events of all sorts, from opera to rock-and-roll, exotic food, moderately intoxicating drinks and the company of a large group of pleasant people.

Sweden does not have an historic tradition of public festivals, like for example Germany or Italy. Our Midsummerfest, however hilarious or exotic it may seem to onlookers, is only a two-day event, spread thinly over the countryside. To succeed in spreading our message to the public we realised that we would have to have a much broader base.

The message itself was simple: enjoy, eat, drink and rub shoulders with your fellow man - it is all for a good cause.

Since its beginning in 1991 the Stockholm Water Festival has grown to become the second biggest event in Europe and one of the fifteen biggest events in the world. It attracts around 1.5 million visitors, paying an average of three visits to the festival area. It boosts services and trade by some 300 million US dollars, sends some 100 million US dollars into the Swedish Treasury in taxes and gives employment opportunities to an undefined number of hitherto unemployed people. It has paid for public education programmes in environmental protection, for planting fish into the waterways, for the construction of sewage treatment plants in nations bordering on the Baltic Sea, for the dissemination of vital information from scientific sources to the public and for instilling a sense of personal responsibility in each citizen concerning water. It has gradually given Europeans a new and improved image of a small nation far up north, a nation that may have an important message for all of us: *take good care of your water.*

This method of *Utile Dulce*, combining necessary work with pleasure, has worked unusually well in Sweden. The Stockholm Water Company, Stockholm's municipal waterworks, has followed up by staging the annual Stockholm Water Symposium, which takes place during the Festival period and thus takes advantage of the opportunity to show the fruits of its own labour to visiting scientists and policy-makers. The Symposium is visited by around 500 participants from more than 50 different nations from all continents. It attracts speakers from all walks of life and tries to encourage new, rather more philosophical and humanistic ways of thinking about water. The Symposium ends with the Stockholm Water Prize Award Ceremony, giving the participants a good excuse to brush the dust off their tuxedos and dance.

The three events, the Prize, the Symposium and the Festival, are now firmly embedded in the Swedish calendar. The Prize enjoys a steadily rising interest from institutions from all over the world, recently illustrated by the inauguration of a 'Bacardi and Stockholm Water Foundation Professorship' at MIT. Another project is the Stockholm

Junior Water Prize, a world-wide schools competition to be launched during what remains of the 20th century.

If there is any lesson to be drawn from this story it must be: 'a spoonful of sugar helps the medicine go down'. An important message attracts far more interest if it is combined with an event that takes national characteristics like pride or guilt or enthusiasm into serious consideration. All this has been achieved over a period of five years and without any funding or grants from either federal or municipal taxes.

We have learned our lesson and it was FUN.

Chapter 4

Valuing the environment

Introduction

Andreas Papandreou

Humans have a special facility of assigning functions to things. Rather than seeing physical objects as merely being, we place them within a context of purposes and ends. In doing so we implicitly value phenomena. Trees are seen to be good for furniture and shade; rivers provide the joys of fishing, they offer a source of irrigation and are used as an assimilator of waste; oceans sustain life forms, provide transport routes as well as wave energy, and regulate the natural environment. In a more religious vein, we may value nature and its creatures as being sacred or providing an image of their 'Creator'.

Many of our individual values conflict. We would like to have cheap oil to heat our homes but we would also like to have oil-free seas and avoid global warming with its consequent harm to future generations. To a large extent, we judge the society in which we live by the way it arbitrates and manages our different and often conflicting ends. When it appears that our society is not doing a good job in guiding our actions, so that we over-fish our oceans or spoil nature's beauty, we might say that the wrong interests are being supported, or that our many values are not being properly weighted, or even that the wrong set of values are being promoted and shaped.

The papers that follow are all concerned with a diverse array of questions pertaining to the way that we as individuals or as a society value the environment.

Professor Yannaras considers whether Christianity instills the right kind of values towards nature. He points out that in the Ancient Greek religious outlook, the paramount virtue was to be in harmony with nature, an order of beauty which 'encompassed the reality of God, who constituted part of its general seemliness'. This quintessentially 'ecological' view of nature, which sees humans as a part of nature and protectors of its beauty, is juxtaposed with the modern utilitarian view of nature as a mere tool to further anthropocentric desires. He discusses how the move from Hellenism to Christianity took two diverging paths. The medieval western European path ultimately paved the way for the modern utilitarian view. In contrast, he describes how the Graeco-Roman tradition presents a smoother transition from Hellenism and maintains an 'ecological' interpretation of nature.

Professor Broome's paper might be said, in part, to consider how we should sharpen our capacity to value the environment and its many services. He contrasts 'two different ways of understanding our responsibilities to the environment'. One appeals to notions of justice, framing our responsibilities towards the environment and its constituents in terms of rights we have, or do not have, to harm natural creatures. The other views our responsibilities in terms of goodness or value, so that we protect the environment because we consider it good to do so. Broome argues that, contrary to our intuition which appeals to justice to provide a more forceful way to protect the environment, a stronger ally will be found when the environment is defended on grounds of it being 'good' to protect the environment.

Professor Despotopoulos emphasises the great threat to humanity from inadequate protection of the natural environment and poses the central challenge that we face: 'our ability to establish reverence towards nature and a measured use of its vital elements'. To meet this challenge we need to overcome our 'ruthless individuality' and to establish institutions of global governance. He warns us of the dangers of the ideology of Progress and Science that take an uncritical view of technological advancement and suggests that scientific research should be tempered in accordance with the ancient Greek attitude of *pan metron ariston* (moderation is best).

Dr Vesely criticises the field of environmental and ecological studies which, he argues, is often nothing more the repackaging of some traditional natural sciences with the appending of the adjective 'environmental', while maintaining their 'instrumental and exploitative' orientation. Furthermore, these 'scientific' approaches tend to boost our confidence in drastically simplified mathematical constructs of reality and our capacity to control it. In a kind of self-prophesying way, they tend to promote 'solutions' to the environmental crisis that, due to their partial nature, become perpetuators of the crises they are meant to cure. Better approaches, Vesely argues, can be found in other disciplines such as architecture. In a sense the 'environmental sciences' promote the wrong values and thereby are inherently incapable of appreciating the values of nature.

Professor Shiva focuses squarely on the crisis in our oceans resulting from over-fishing. This crisis is seen as resulting primarily from the collapse in life-sustaining ethical values. She argues that the promotion of the market paradigm has been eroding those very 'traditional' values that have sustained the commons. Local communities have evolved ethical rules of managing their common and 'free' oceans that are sensitive both to the biological diversity of the seas as well as to the sustenance of the fishing community. The solution to this ocean crisis is a return of the local resources to the local communities and a reaffirmation of the values of the commons.

Existential versus Regulative Approaches to the Problem of the Environment. The Environmental Issue: an Existential not a Canonical Problem

Christos Yannaras

The Apocalypse of St John has been regarded as the supreme symbol of the decisive cultural shift which occurred in human history with the advent of Christianity: a shift from *nature* to *History*. The problem of the environment - the violation of nature, its unrestrained exploitation by the human race - is judged to be a necessary consequence of the priority which Christianity gave to history, subordinating nature to an eschatological perspective which entailed its final disappearance for the sake of an eagerly awaited spiritual 'Kingdom'.

We are speaking of a 'cultural shift' because Christianity was preceded by Ancient Greece. To the Greeks the idea of the historicity of nature was unknown. The problem of a beginning in time and a predetermined end did not arise. Nature constituted the fullness of *being*: a beautiful structure of harmony and order which rendered it a *cosmo-cosmema*, an ordered ornament. A perfect universe, harmoniously arranged, with a given absolute rationality, it even encompassed the reality of God, who constituted a part of its general seemliness. Given that the world was eternal, it could not have any goal other than itself. It could only *be*. And the greatest thing that human beings could attain was to *contemplate* and to *imitate* the perfection of the cosmos. Knowledge of the cosmos, *episteme* was identified with virtue, the serene *prudence* that came from participating in the universal 'common mind' or logos. The collective imitation of the harmony of the cosmos formed 'the microcosm of the city', the common effort of *political life*, which did not differ from the art of the composer or the painter, since it aimed at the same imitation of the laws of the rationality which beautified the universe. What was of the first importance to the Greeks was not '*becoming*' or '*the necessary*', was not potentiality and will, but '*being*' and its rational plenitude.

Modern Europe saw the appearance of Christianity - chiefly through the eyes of Hegel, Fichte and Schelling - as a radical break in the Greek view of nature. The God of the Judaeo-Christian tradition is outside the cosmos. He himself creates the cosmos, giving it a specific temporal beginning and directing it towards a preordained end. Now it is History that has priority not nature, the *'becoming'* of nature not the *'being'* of nature. This historicity of nature is at the outset devalued because it is dominated by the consequence of the 'fall' and sin of humanity. Human beings are called upon to participate in History - in God's plan for the salvation of humanity - and they succeed in the measure in which they are liberated from nature and the necessity of the laws of the fall which held sway over nature. In this perspective, the book of the Apocalypse of St John was interpreted as a radical and final condemnation of nature, since the expected eschatological 'Kingdom' is announced as a nightmare of physical destruction and the collapse of the entire universe. Thus the world is presented as a simple episode in a *History* which essentially undermines it and finally destroys it. The expression 'this world' becomes synonymous with the expression 'this age' and signifies a particular historical period, and 'age' which is inimical and contrary to the 'age which is to come' of the Kingdom of God.

Was the Christian view of nature in reality so radically contrary to the Greek view? Let us put this question to one side for the moment, for I should like to address the second vital 'shift' in our encounter within nature which has been accomplished within the framework of our modern attitudes, our contemporary culture.

This culture was founded by the philosophy of the Enlightenment on a polemical opposition to metaphysics. The opposition expressed a historical need after the painful medieval experience of centuries in the course of which metaphysics were transformed into a dominant ideology of an integral character.

The opposition of our modern culture to metaphysics - the shedding of religious integralism - appeared as an enthusiastic affirmation of nature and the potentialities of nature. It was concerned above all with the knowledge of physical reality, not with its metaphysical supports. It was concerned with humanity, not with people as creator and image of God, but as physical entities, physical individuals. It was concerned with enhancing the value of physical existence and life, not with a morality supported by threats of eternal punishment, but with a conformity to the rationality of nature, a 'Natural Law' which would guarantee the *rights* of every physical individual.

The nature-centred 'shift', however, which modern culture has enshrined, did not entail a return to the ancient Greek interpretation of the world as a measure of rational harmony and plenitude - even though such a return was pursued by the humanists of the West, who worshipped everything Greek. Certainly the character of the only assured interpretation of reality was attributed to nature; the measure and axis of its rational reality was only individual human subjectivity. The rational self-awareness of the human subject was regarded as the only foundation of reality which could not be shaken by doubt.

The nature-centered shift of our modern culture has proved to be anthropocentric, not cosmocentric. Western European man discovered the universe of objective existents with youthful enthusiasm but as master and proprietor. 'I understand means I possess', wrote the young Hegel in his *Early Theological Writings (Theologische Jugendschriften).* The individual understanding decodes the rationality of nature, intervenes in its powers to draw out a result useful and beneficial to man. Nature in the modern view is a useful object and knowledge, *episteme* is authority.

In this way the concept and imperative of *progress* is introduced for the first time into human History. This no longer has any relationship with the Christian interpretation of the development of History towards a final end of apocalyptic fulfilment. Progress is now the constant extension of the mastery of the human powers of production in the whole of nature. Progress is measured by indicators of productivity and ease of consumption, the economy subordinates politics and every social dynamic and proves to be the exclusive factor and only criterion of social 'development'.

Res extensa - res cogitans: the antithetical distinction between man and nature was set out by Descartes who guided medieval scholastic thought to its unforeseen but inevitable consequences. Kant will also interiorise even the objective external world in the subjective reason: 'Outside myself nothing exists except within my own discernment.' One step further and Hegel will see in the human tool a 'meta-physics' and in technology a 'materialised metaphysics'. He will announce that 'we are much closer to the spirit when we make a tool than when we give birth to a child'. And in absolute accord with the idealist Hegel, the materialist Marx will assert that 'the history of industry is the open book of the essential powers of man, the human psychology which is perceived experimentally'.

From these theoretical opinions to the practice of the violation of nature by technology is but a small step. That is why it seems at least paradoxical that we seek a solution to the problems of the environment today relying on the guide-lines set by a culture of 'modernity' which has led with an iron inevitability to the destruction of the natural environment which now threatens us.

Let us return to the question which we left in abeyance. Was the Christian view of nature in reality so antithetical to the Greek? Is the Apocalypse of St John a triumph of History over nature, the proclamation of the final denigration and destruction of nature for the sake of the messianic Kingdom.

Both questions pose problems of interpretation of the relation and differences between Hellenism and Christianity, and together with these a problem of criteria for understanding the symbolism of the Apocalypse. Hermeneutic differences are not always exhausted on the theoretical level: they can lead also to total transformations of cultures, as happened in Europe in the 11th century. In that period the Graeco-Roman world (the Byzantine world, as we would say today) understood its relationship with Christianity in a manner very different from the way in which the Germanic peoples of central and western Europe understood their relationship both with the Greek and with the Christian tradition.

In the History of Philosophy hermeneutic problems become insoluble if we overlook the discontinuity brought about by that critical rupture in the development of European civilisation which we call the 'Great Migration of Peoples', that is to say, if we overlook the fact that from the end of the fourth century until the sixth century AD the greater part of Europe was subjected to a cultural reverse which was literally tragic in comparison with its Graeco-Roman past. The new tribes which migrated and established themselves in Europe at that time - Franks, Goths, Huns, Vandals, Burgundians, Normans - were on a cultural level which was markedly low, if not downright primitive.

The first civilising step was their conversion to Christianity. But what could conversion mean to peoples who had not even the elementary presuppositions of education for the understanding of the Greek philosophical forms in which Christian experience was expressed? It was inevitable that they would adapt the understanding of Christianity to the level of their own criteria and needs.

In every situation of cultural backwardness in History, the interpretation of the existent and the pragmatic - which endows with meaning the relations between human begins and nature, their fellow human beings and God - becomes a schematic simplification, usually strongly polarised between distinctions of 'good' and 'evil' and is consequently juristic and legal. A characteristic example in Judaic history, for example, is the decline of the Talmudic tradition into pharisaic legalism, or, in the later Hellenistic period, the transmutation of Platonic dualism into Manichean Gnosticism.

For this historical assertion to be properly supported with evidence a special monograph would be needed. Here it is only put forward as a proposal offering a criterion for interpreting the differences distinguishing the Graeco-Roman from the medieval western European version of relations between Hellenism and Christianity. This second version, the medieval western European, was inherited for the most part by the modern world. In his study of Nietzsche, Heidegger demonstrated clearly the inevitable continuity (*Kontinuität*) of the metaphysics of the western Middle Ages for the theistic and atheistic systems of modern times.

In this short address it is worth touching briefly on some basic theses of the Graeco-Roman version of relations between Hellenism and Christianity, particularly on what concerns the problem of nature and History which is directly localised in the Apocalypse of St John.

Certainly Christianity denies the eternity of the world. But is this element fundamental in treating of ancient Greek cosmology? When the problem of a beginning and an end of the world is not posed, the property of the eternal (the 'ever advancing') relates mainly to the ubiquitous rationality with which the world, independently of time and period, is offered to the vision-contemplation of the human person.

The fundamental distinguishing mark of ancient Greek cosmology is not the eternity of the world, but the recognition of a universal common rational principle (*xynos logos*) which articulates, structures and governs physical or natural reality. This logos forms the universe into a cosmos - an ordered harmony and beauty. The logos-mode of participation in being distinguishes the *essences* of existents, shapes the variety of *forms*, formulates the *laws* of the order and harmony, of the coexistence and movement of beings. The logos-form is the 'lover' of matter, the motive (the appetitive aspect) which urges matter to the movement which gives it form, to the *entelechy* of endowment with form.

This *'logical'* composition and function of the world is neither denied nor destroyed by Christianity. Christianity only interprets it, revealing the uninterpreted gaps of ancient Greek ontology. The logos which brings together, constructs and governs the universe is not an independent given which ends up as blind fate. It is the personal energy of a creating Person, the created result of an uncreated transcendent First Principle. Uncreated and therefore timeless and infinite - that is the existence of God; created and therefore temporal and finite - that is the nature of the world.

The human personal existence, however, of the painter, the sculptor, the composer, is of a different essence from that of painting, sculpture and song. And just as painting, sculpture and song do not cease to be a logos revelatory of the personal otherness and freedom of the creator-artist, so too the world, in spite of its *essential* difference from God does not cease to be a logos revelatory of his Person.

This is a supreme measure of the ecological, as we would say today, attitude of humanity towards nature: For the Christian, nature is not an impersonal and neutral object, even though created by some Supreme Being. Nature is the artefact of a personal God-Logos which reveals in every fold the personal otherness of the creative energy of its maker. The term 'natural contemplation' in the Christian vocabulary refers to the result of ascetic self-transcendence, the ascetic achievement of our transcending our egocentric, acquisitive and exploitative priorities, and our living our relationship with the world in the way we live our relationship with a painted, sculptured, musical or whatever other work of art.

The human person is called not to a one-sided contemplation of the world but to a personal relationship with the logos of the cosmos, because this logos is called to a communion of life with the Creator of the world. The use of the world - food, clothing, tools - is in one way or another a life-giving prerequisite for humanity. This use, however, which serves the daily survival of the created human being can bring about a relationship of communion with God. The appropriation of nature by the human person in order that he should exist, not in the manner of created nature, but in the manner of relationship, of loving communion, is the mode of existence of the Uncreated - for 'God is love' (1 John 4:16).

This is the sense of *Eucharist* which constitutes and forms the Church and gives meaning to the practice of the Christian life. In the Eucharist Christians receive nature, the cosmos, as food in a direct way - as bread and wine, two kinds of food which encapsulate the things necessary for the sustenance of human life. They receive them 'with Thanksgiving' as gifts of God and this receiving constitutes a communion of human beings with God, a cosmic flesh of divine communion. In every Eucharist Christians communicate the flesh of the incarnate Logos, the Logos who became flesh within History as the first-fruit of the power of created nature to exist in the mode of the fullness of life of the Uncreated.

The 'ecology' of the Christian Church is the endowment of the world with meaning through the Eucharist and the eucharistic use of the world. This use, however, is not an existential necessity: it constantly takes risks in the existential adventure of the *freedom* of the human person. The book of the Apocalypse uses a striking poetic iconography to picture this current adventure and its eschatological goal, which is ceaselessly fulfilled and is intended to be accomplished not only as the destruction of nature and end of time, but as the restoration of nature and time in a fulfilling communion of life with created and uncreated being, in a universal Eucharist.

The way out from today's ecological blind alleys cannot be accomplished as long as our culture remains tied to the anthropocentric utilitarianism of the modern world and to its medieval religious roots. A different reading of the Apocalypse of John is indispensable for the formation of a view of the relations between *nature* and *History* which will lead to new criteria with respect to the way the world is used.

Value versus Justice, and the Uses of Economics

John Broome

I want to start by distinguishing two different ways of understanding our responsibilities to the environment. On the one hand, we might think of our responsibilities in terms of justice and rights. We might think that nature, or individual species, or individual animals, or ecologies have a right to be preserved or not to be harmed. Or we might think that future generations have a right to receive the earth from us in good condition. Thinking like this supposes that, as a matter of justice, we owe it to natural creatures or future generations not to harm them; they have rights that we ought not to infringe.

Alternatively, we can think of our responsibilities in terms of goodness or value. It is simply a bad thing if we harm nature or future people. We make future people's lives and perhaps our own less good than they might have been; we make the world a less good place. We ought not to cause harm and make things worse and that is why we ought to preserve the environment. This is quite a different type of reason for caring about the environment. It appeals to the virtue of benevolence rather than the virtue of justice. We should consider the interests of future generations, it says, not because we owe it to them as a matter of right but because we ought to do good for people and avoid causing harm.

Appealing to justice is in a way more powerful than appealing to benevolence. Benevolence is a virtue and one ought to be benevolent. If a person acts unjustly and infringes the rights of others, we may throw him or her into prison, which shows how seriously we regard it, but not if he or she merely lacks benevolence. So when people argue for protecting the environment, it is natural for them to do it in terms of justice and rights. They say that leaving nuclear waste in the water or dumping greenhouse gases in the air infringes the rights of future people, and for that reason we should not do it. They say that future people have a right to an unpolluted planet and that is why we ought to leave an unpolluted planet to them.

I think this is a mistake. Many people find it implausible that plants or ecosystems have rights and will not be impressed by arguments that assume they do. However, even if they do not have rights, it does not follow that it is alright to harm them. Harming them may be doing bad, even if it is not infringing rights. If we concentrate on our responsibilities to future generations of people we may find more convincing reasons for behaving well towards the environment. I think we should leave future people an unpolluted planet because pollution makes the lives of future people less good and makes the world a worse place than it would have been. We ought not to do it for the good of future people, not because of their rights.

I find it hard to believe future people have a right to an unpolluted planet for several reasons. I shall try to explain only one of them. It is the sort of finicky point that impresses philosophers but may seem sophistical to others; however, I shall risk it because it impresses me. It was, I believe, first noticed by the philosopher Derek Parfit. Suppose we decide to control pollution more severely than we are doing. Suppose we institute new policies to control the release of greenhouse gases, for instance. These policies will make a significant difference to people's lives. Carbon taxes, for instance, will noticeably increase the cost of travel, so people will travel less. Their social contacts will be a bit different, and many people will end up with different spouses and partners. They will have children at different times, and that means having different children from those they would have had had the tax not been imposed. After only a generation or two, the people who will be alive, if we control pollution, will be entirely different people from those who would be alive if we did not.

If future people have a right to an unpolluted planet and if nevertheless we pollute the planet, we must have infringed the rights of the people who are alive in the future. But there is no way we could have done anything better for those people. Had we not polluted, those people would not even have existed; a different lot of people would have existed instead. It is hard to believe we could have infringed the rights of future people if the only other thing we could have done would have prevented their existence altogether.

If, however, we switch our attention to the domain of value, we may find a more convincing reason for behaving well towards the environment: If we pollute, people's lives will be less good than they would have been had we not polluted and the world will be a less good place.

For this reason, I think our arguments about the environment should be focused on goodness or value rather than rights and justice. And this is where I come to economics. Economics is not much good at justice but it can help with the analysis of some aspects of value, particularly with the good of human beings. Economics has tools to help us analyse how good or bad the future will be. It is by no means easy to know what is for the best in environmental matters. We cannot simply say: don't pollute. Whatever we do, we will pollute. Nothing will prevent the accumulation of greenhouse gases in the atmosphere. We can control them to a greater or lesser extent, that is all. Controlling them severely will require significant sacrifices on the part of present people, for the sake of improving the lives of future people. So sacrifices to present people must be balanced against benefits to future people. Some extreme sacrifices we could make would definitely not be worthwhile. We must weigh up the benefits against the costs. That is the sort of thing economics is good at.

However, the methods of economics have often been misapplied. Economists are pig-headed in some ways and their pig-headedness sometimes shows in environmental economics. Suppose there is a plan to destroy or risk destroying a Pacific atoll with its lagoon. How should we attach a value to what is destroyed? In the bad old days economists tended to count only the tangible harms to people. People who live on the island will have to move; potential visitors may have to keep away. Traditionally the harm to the islanders is measured by the amount of money that would need to be paid to compensate them fully. Since the people directly affected may be rather few, the harm measured this way may be small.

Against this conclusion, sensible people claimed that surely the island, with all its animals and plants, has a value in itself, quite apart from its usefulness to the people directly affected. Now the bad old days are over, economists take account of the value of the island's being there (the 'non-use value') as well. So this is a step in the right direction. But how do they assess this value? The standard way in principle is this: they find out from people around the world how much money they would be willing to pay to preserve the island if they could, and add up all these willingnesses to pay. The idea is that each person's willingness to pay measures the value of the island to that person, and we are interested in its value to people in total.

It should come as no surprise that the answers people in practice give to questions like 'What would you be willing to pay to preserve this island?' make little sense. For instance, it turns out that people often mention about the same figure if they are asked about a single island or about a whole archipelago. Nor does the question separate the value of the island to a person from the person's estimate of its value for its own sake. The question also assumes that people somehow know the value of a thing such as an island naturally. But it is extremely hard to know the value of an island and a figure that a person pulls out of the air is likely to have no interest. Economists approach the question this way because they are committed to a particular theory of value: that value arises only from people s preferences and that preferences can be measured by willingness to pay. But this is a rotten theory and economics will have to give it up before its methods can make a useful contribution to valuing the environment.

However, once the methods of economics are stripped of this encumbrance, they can contribute a battery of formal techniques that are excellently suited to the problems of weighing and balancing values. Different policies we might adopt to protect the environment distribute value differently in the world. Some policies achieve some values better, others other values, and these values need to be weighed. Controlling global warming for the sake of future generations, for example, will be a burden to us. The present and the future need to be weighed against each other. It is by no means settled how this should be done. Economists and others debate whether the future should be discounted, which means counting the well-being of future people for less than our own well-being.

Discounting is by no means the hardest problem of weighing that global warming raises. Rising sea levels will expose millions of people to increased risk of flooding in Bangladesh and other low-lying areas. Tropical diseases are also likely to extend their range, and will kill people in millions. So one benefit of controlling greenhouse gases will be to save lives in the future. The saving of lives needs to be weighed against the sacrifices we are called on to make.

Moreover, global warming will undoubtedly alter the world's population in a way that is not easily predictable. Many millions of people will be forced to migrate from Bangladesh and elsewhere, as the places where they live become uninhabitable. Movements of population on this scale cannot happen without affecting the size of population. So we need to evaluate changes in population too - another value that needs to be put into the calculations.

We have no solutions to these problems. They are problems about value that need to be faced if we are to know how to respond properly to the problems of the environment. The methods of economics can provide an analytical framework for working on them.

Contemporary Civilisation and Natural Environment

Constantine I Despotopoulos

The failure of this modern age to protect the integrity of our natural environment is the primary and great threat to humanity.

Since early times man's activities have affected nature. Our nourishment and survival are impossible without effecting changes in the natural environment. Agriculture, although appropriately described as 'cultivation of the land', has always caused a certain amount of damage; quarrying and mining have caused even more. Man's intensely corrosive influence on his natural environment has been, and still is, a symptom of the promotion of so-called 'civilisation'. Though industry is valuable and indispensable for over-populated mankind, it is also destructive of the natural environment; it can destroy not only the ground it uses for its installations, but also the water and the atmosphere of the areas which surround it.

Until recent times, man's destructive effect on his natural environment has been more or less manageable, since its extent was limited compared to the magnitude of the seas, the size of the continents and what was thought to be a limitless supply of raw materials. But the situation is different today. There are many examples in our time that refute the previously widespread notion that nature can be exploited without mercy. The intense pollution of the atmosphere and water in many areas of the globe, due to the demands of over-developed industry or of dense communications networks, particularly the transportation of large quantities of oil, is one example. Yet another is the approaching exhaustion of natural reserves of very useful raw materials, as in the destruction of forests either as a waste product of industry, or by direct deforestation in order to obtain cultivatable lands.

The question for us is this: in our era does mankind have the ability to establish reverence towards nature and a measured use of its vital elements? The answer does not encourage optimism. There are many reasons today for the immense difficulty of instilling a reverential attitude towards the natural environment and towards the economic use of natural resources. A primary reason is the over-population of mankind. Another cause is the poverty of the majority of people on earth, but also the luxurious lifestyles of those in wealthy countries. Furthermore, there is the speculative greed of gigantic financial institutions in inexorable competition amongst themselves, in accordance with society's overwhelming emphasis on 'Mammon's Law'. Another reason is the creation and existence of huge stockpiles of arms which consume precious raw materials and are therefore active accessories in the abuse of mankind's natural resources. An additional factor is the result of the idolatry of technology, the irresistible tendency of our societies to create huge constructions which sometimes affect the land to a great depth and always consume precious physical resources.

Our task, therefore, if we are to succeed in effectively protecting the physical environment, is to fight against all these trends while at the same time providing effective education for all the peoples of the world.

There are many questions to be addressed. How can we control over-population as long as there is a mass of independent states and the almost scandalously unequal distribution of economic resources and educational benefits among the various peoples? How are we to reduce arms to a minimum in an atmosphere of nationalist antagonism and other forms of animosity or distrust? How can we persuade the wealthy inhabitants of economically developed countries to deny themselves their present life of luxury which results in the deprivation of people in poor countries and also in the denial of resources to future generations? How are the inhabitants of wealthy countries going to be persuaded to shoulder the responsibility of global economising? Would this be easier if they thought of themselves as part of a global family who have to economise and limit the consumption of materials out of global solidarity? Would they be prepared to reduce their own consumption of luxuries?

Are we going to manage to condense the vast air and other communications networks by eliminating routes which do not serve vital needs? Are we going to ban tankers whose size surpasses the capacity of existing waste-handling technology, so that in the event of a serious oil spill any damage to the natural environment can be avoided? How, generally speaking, are the gigantic economic institutions going to be prevented from abusing mankind's wealth in natural resources, when their unofficial authority very often neutralises the official authority of the political leaders of the nations?

What is required is an almost superhuman effort in order to overcome the ruthless individualism dominating the behaviour of men. It is also necessary for a strong political authority to be established across the boundaries of states, working in close co-operation with governments to create an attitude of reverence towards nature amongst all peoples. Governments or some other nominated organisation will have to impose the necessary draconian decisions on a global scale. This is an apt modern mission for Christian morality, particularly with its focus on the protection of the physical environment. This would be another brave and critical mission of genuine political action at a global level.

In addition to all that has been mentioned so far, we must also consider the major source of danger to mankind in our era and how we can deal with this supreme threat.

Our era has inherited two enticing idols from the late 18th and the 19th centuries: Progress and Science. Applied science is still revered and scientific research and experimentation is still considered almost sacred and inviolable, contributing to the progress of mankind. Unquestionably, some of the scientific research being carried out during our era is precious and an indispensable condition for the improvement of technology. It is more necessary today than during any other era for the increase of production and the provision of vital resources for the survival of mankind. However, the extreme ideology which favours unlimited experimental research may prove fatal to the very existence of mankind.

Since the middle of our century scientists have carried out experiments using physical powers of immense size, which have the capacity to violate the resistance of the physical environment. The abominable ethos of this research, along with the shameful syndrome of neglecting the health and lives of people involved and affected, is concealed by the misleading and anachronistic ideology of the quasi-sacredness of science.

For the past 40 years I have repeatedly argued that scientific research, in some of its more hazardous forms, constitutes for the first time in history a source of devilish danger for the human race. This unprecedented danger could include the total extinction of mankind, or of a large proportion of it, because of the unforeseen result of a scientific experiment carried out with unknown neo-titanic forces released thoughtlessly from nature, or as a result of the initiative of a master criminal or a madman. In addition to this supreme danger, a new danger has appeared which slowly undermines the health and the intelligence of men, the unrecognised side-effects of the numerous applications in our lives of these demonic inventions.

The objection that danger has always been inherent in scientific experiments, but is tolerated as a necessary price to be paid for the progress of science in benefiting mankind, ignores a critical difference. In the past, the only ones to risk danger were the members of the experimental team. In our era, there is a great possibility that the whole human race, or a large part of it, may disappear. Therefore scientists today should espouse the teachings of Greek wisdom - *meden agan* (nothing in excess), *metron ariston* (moderation is best) - and adopt the motto of Aristotle - *anagi stinai* (necessity to stop) - especially when their experiments may cause the uncontrolled release of huge physical forces. Experiments which have such a potentially horrendous outcome must be banned globally by all states.

On the contrary, we should encourage responsible and productive scientific research carried out on a theoretical basis, using mathematics, or research which is carried out with the goal of extending our knowledge of nature, provided it does not create the danger of releasing uncontrollable forces of huge dimensions.

Undoubtedly it is very difficult to define in advance which research experiments will include excessive danger and should be banned and which experimental research is to be allowed and should be supported. However, this distinction is critical for mankind and constitutes a problem to be solved by the wise men of our era.

On the other hand, it is very difficult to adopt and uphold the verdict of wisdom as to the limit of scientific experimental research, even when wise men of great prestige have been involved. One reason for this almost insurmountable difficulty is the still widespread ideology of the sacredness of scientific research. There is also the limitless ambition of some scientific researchers, the speculative greed of some large financial institutions which initiate dangerous experiments, the trend towards further development of armaments, stemming from the fear of some states of their enemies or from the megalomania of their political leadership. Above all, there are no political authorities throughout the world who are sufficiently clear sighted, brave and popular, and with a commitment to caring for the life of all mankind, to enforce their decisions globally.

It is to be hoped, however, that awareness of this supreme danger may contribute to bringing humanity to its senses and the states of the world to a timely and active agreement in order to meet this vital challenge which is critical for the survival of mankind in our era.

The Ecology of Inhabited Space

Dalibor Vesely

I suppose that anybody who surveys today the field of ecological or environmental studies must feel rather bewildered. On one side are studies called 'environmental', which up to now have existed under a different name and do not have much to do directly with the environment; on the other side are studies and projects which do not necessarily use the adjective 'environmental', but represent a genuine contribution to the understanding and creation of environment, sustainable not only in terms of pure survival but also culturally. To the first category belong, as an example, traditional natural sciences, slightly modified and renamed without any real change of their instrumental, exploitative orientation. In the second category we can find, again as an example, landscape and garden design, architecture and urban or civic design. However, the adjectives and labels are not as important as is the nature of thinking or making, characteristic for each particular discipline, and on a more general level for our everyday knowledge and activities.

The so-called 'environmental crisis' is a complex phenomenon but we know that it is an artificially created one, and that its main source is the discrepancy between the partiality of experimental knowledge turned into production and the given reality. The main characteristic of modern experimental knowledge is the possibility to create a fully independent representation of reality as a foundation of knowledge which is universal, that is, universally applicable and effective but unfortunately also relevant only to a small segment of reality and with an enigmatic relation to that reality. The imaginary character of experimental knowledge is well described in the following statement:

> For a short time, therefore, allow your thought to leave this world in order to come to see a wholly new one, which I shall cause to be born in the presence of your thought in imaginary spaces.[1]

The same author tells us not only what is possible but what is also seriously anticipated:

> By science, I understand skill at resolving all questions and in inventing by one's own industry everything in that science that can be invented by human ingenuity (*ars inveniendi*). Whoever has this science does not desire much else foreign to it, and indeed is quite properly called *autarches* - self sufficient.[2]

This unusual confidence has its origin in the drastically simplified representation of reality which became possible because of the deep faith in the mathematical and predictable nature of reality.

We do not yet fully understand the real nature of experimental knowledge on which modern science and technology are based because it is difficult to follow the transformation of reality and its representation through a construct from which all but efficient causes have been eliminated and where the qualitative diversity of phenomena has been reduced to a mathematical representation of reified processes. There is quite clearly a gap between the productive knowledge and the reality of the natural world. This gap which represents a radical discontinuity with the world is a permanent source of environmental crisis. The permanence of the crisis is directly linked to another dilemma - discontinuity between too many good intentions to understand and improve the environment and the inadequacy of knowledge on which such intentions are based, to say nothing about the slowly changing attitudes and the nature of our activities. We tend to speak about the environment as a continuum which does not have particular boundaries and about ecology as a unified science, and yet we do not have a discipline which can seriously address such issues in their wholeness. To understand the qualitative structure and meaning of the phenomenal world through cosmology or philosophy of nature as it was possible in the past is not available to us today.[3]

It is true of course that some of the current ecological studies address reality on the world scale, particularly in the areas of pollution, global warming, resources and population. However, the total picture, despite its apparent sense of wholeness, is inevitably partial. It is one thing to speak about pollution for instance in terms of quantifiable levels of emission and its reduction but it is a very different thing to understand how is pollution linked with the economic, political, social or cultural realities. The lack of a more comprehensive understanding of the main environmental issues motivated the recent shift from a shallow to a so-called 'deep ecology'. Unfortunately, despite all the promises and positive effort, deep ecology has not yet discovered its structure or paradigm and remains so far only a loose, well-intentioned movement.[4]

This brings us back to the disciplines which are not usually considered to be in the centre of current ecological studies and yet their contribution to the understanding and improvement of the global environment could be vital. A good example is architecture, which served for millennia as a measure of the limits of human interference with nature (natural conditions). I am thinking particularly about the role of cities in their relationship to surrounding countryside (nature) and to the more abstract achievements in the domain of religion, politics, arts, crafts and knowledge. There is no doubt that cities represent the most complex environment ever created and that most of the civilisational changes, as well as our attitudes to reality, were initiated there. It is well known that even the radical commitments to unspoilt nature and wilderness are almost without exception formed in the context of urban culture. In the long history of architectural thinking, what we call today environment was referred to as a space seen at first as a situated configuration of places or as a setting, and more recently as a situational structure of the world in which our culture is embodied.[5]

In the situational understanding of reality the distinction between internal and external world disappears and with it also the notion of environment as a characteristic of the external world. If we start from ourselves it is quite clearly difficult to say what is and what is not environment. Are we, as corporeal beings, in the environment or rather an indivisible part of it? Is it not true that our bodies are also an environment of our feelings, imagination and thought? The problem of environment thus appears as a problem of embodiment and our environmental crisis as a crisis of embodiment, which can be more precisely described as a discontinuity or conflict between the embodied and disembodied phenomena, events and structures of our world. Because the disembodiment is a result of our inventiveness and unconditional productivity, we have to admit, that we ourselves are the environmental crisis.

The space of our existence and co-existence, seen as a situational structure of our world, is probably the most plausible paradigm for future ecological studies that is available to us today. The virtue of this paradigm is its capacity to support not only the understanding but also the making of the world. There is a growing awareness that the current ecological crisis has its economic, political, social and cultural conditions but that its main source is our way of life and our values. Knowledge, better understanding and persuasion, have obviously their place in influencing our attitudes but they cannot substitute the power of the reality in which we live our everyday life. It is here that the making of the world and particularly the making of our cities, where in a short time the majority of the world's population is likely to live, will be of primary importance for any future ecological considerations.

1 R Descartes, *Oeuvres*, tome XI, Paris Tannery 1975, p.31

2 *ibid.*, tome III, p.722

3 Such possibility became problematic already in the eighteenth century due to a specialisation of knowledge and formation of new disciplines. In this process, traditional cosmology was reduced into a specialised science of astronomy. The philosophy of nature became under this condition only an accessory discipline which was eventually in the course of the nineteenth century entirely discredited.

[4] M Oelschlaeger, *The Ideal Wilderness*, Yale University Press, 1991, p.302. A Naess, 'The Deep Ecological Movement. Some Philosophical Aspects' in *Environmental Philosophy*, edited by M E Zimmerman, Prentice Hall, New Jersey 07632, 1993, p.193

[5] M Merleau-Ponty, *Phenomenology of Perception*, Routledge Kegan Paul, 1974, pp.243-299. S B Mallin, *Merleau-Ponty's Philosophy*, Yale University Press, 1979, pp.7-40

Which Value for Nature?

Vandana Shiva

The ocean has been used as a metaphor in diverse cultures for awakening human society to the causes and consequences of disaster brought about by a collapse in the ethical values that sustain life. The Apocalypse in St John's Revelation has served as such a source of awakening. In India, the metaphor of destruction is the *Pralaya*, or dissolution. As described in the *Vishnu Purana*, the world is destroyed and recreated by the cosmic being when human values fail to maintain nature and society. Then Vishnu the Creator assumes the character of Rudra or Shiva the Destroyer and descends to reunite all his creatures with himself. He enters into the seven rays of the sun, drinks up all the waters of the earth, leaving the seas and the springs dry.

Among the degradation of values that brings forth this dissolution is the reduction of all value to wealth and the exclusion of compassion from human relationships. As the *Vishnu Purana* states, 'The minds of men will be wholly occupied in acquiring wealth, and wealth will be spent solely on selfish gratification ... The people will almost always be in dread of dearth and apprehensive of scarcity'.[1]

These links between greed, scarcity and total destruction are at the heart of the ecological crisis which engulfs us. The reduction of all value to monetary value is identified as an important aspect of the crisis of scarcity generated by the very process of increasing affluence.

It is often stated that the roots of environmental destruction lie in our treating natural resources as 'free' and in giving them 'value'. In the dominant paradigm, value is reduced to market price, forgetting that value is derived also from non-tangible sources such as the sacred and from resources held as commons; and such value is too high to be placed at the mercy of the market-place.

For most ancient cultures, the highest form of value in nature has been embodied in the idea of the sacred - sacred forests, sacred rivers, sacred seas have been the cultural and spiritual strategies of assigning a high value to nature and its protection. For the traditional fishermen in Kerala in India, for example, the sea is *Kodalamma* - mother and goddess who offers limitless wealth, if she is revered.

Traditional fishing communities have well worked codes of conduct to ensure justice and sustainability in harvesting the bounties of the ocean. These unwritten rules protect the oceans as a regulated commons. Even today, half the fish consumed comes from communities using the seas as commons, using technologies that protect species diversity and livelihoods, whilst providing fish for local communities rather than global markets.

Spiritual value, ecological common sense and social justice come together in a value system that limits exploitation. It is this very value system that has been identified as 'backwardness and primitiveness' in the 'Mare Liberium' or 'freedom of the seas' paradigm propounded by Hugo Grotius in 1608, according to which the fishery resources are so abundant, they can be exploited freely without fear of depletion.

For traditional fishing communities the seas are 'free' in both a spiritual sense and in the social sense that they belong to none, and ought to be denied to none. The clash in values brought forth by the crises in fisheries is also a clash over which freedom humanity will promote - the freedom of capital to exploit nature or the freedom of nature and people to sustain themselves.

The recognition of nature's 'value' can therefore take place at many levels leading to diverse paradigms and actions: the cosmological, spiritual valuation leads to a rejuvenation of spiritual traditions; the social valuation leads to a recovery of the commons; while the commercial valuation leads to the programme of privatisation, marketisation and commodification of all resources.

This conversion of the sacred and the commons into a commodity has been at the root of the fisheries crisis that we observe in every ocean. Nine of the world's major fishing grounds are threatened. Four have been 'fished out' commercially. The FAO now acknowledges that an estimated 70 per cent of global fish stocks are 'depleted' or 'almost depleted' and that 'the oceans most valuable commercial species are fished to capacity'. This over exploitation of fish in a price-based paradigm destroys both the marine diversity that is necessary to renew the life of the oceans, and the livelihoods of traditional fishing communities whose resources are either usurped or destroyed.

The destruction of marine biodiversity

Technologies such as purse seining and trawling are powerful but destructive. Highly capitalised trawler fleets and purse seiners use nets which scoop up whole shoals of fish among which are 'by-catch' and 'discards': commercially useless because they are the wrong species or the wrong size. As the recent issue of the *Ecologist* reports, annual global discards in commercial fisheries have been conservatively estimated at 27 million tonnes - equivalent to more than one third the weight of all reported marine landings in commercial fisheries world-wide.

The diverse species treated as waste by global commercial fishing fleets is the economic base for the traditional fisherman, and the ecological base for the sustainability of the marine environment.

It is estimated that 100 million of the world's poorest people depend on fishing for all or part of their livelihoods. According to an FAO estimate, there are two million small scale boats and one million large scale boats: it is the latter that cause the problem of over-fishing. Most of the large fishing vessels are controlled by trans-national corporations and possess technology for fish detection, catching and processing, allowing them to become more efficient hunting machines: huge catches are made, but at the high price of destroying the livelihoods of traditional fishing communities through the ecological impact of undermining their very basis.

Catches of fish world-wide plummeted for traditional fishing communities; taking India as an example, sardines and mackerel, once the mainstay of the fisheries, fell from 250,000 tonnes in 1968 to 87,000 tonnes in 1990. This situation is replicated globally, resulting in small fishermen throughout the world organising themselves to protect their right to fish.

On 23-24 November 1994, one million fish workers from nine maritime Indian states covering a coastline of over 7,500 km went on strike. They were protesting against Indian government policies giving international joint ventures free access to fish in the country's Exclusive Economic Zone (EEZ).

Based on a narrow definition of 'productivity', fishing technologies are relentlessly destroying the livelihood of millions; taking into account the criteria of the sustainability and diversity of fish yields, these commercial technologies are in reality very unproductive and wasteful.

The Vice President for Sustainability at the World Bank, Ismail Serageldin has been stating recently that the depletion of marine fisheries will allow us to move from 'primitive' hunting technologies to farming of fish. However, given the recent experience with intensive aquaculture, there is little indication that cultivation of fish guided only by maximising of global commercial value of selected species will be sustainable. Sustainability needs to take diversity of occupations and species into account. It also needs to see production in a longer time frame that is usually considered by commercial interests or economic experts at the World Bank.

The shrimp and fish culture project of the World Bank (1991) is an example of the financing of ecological disaster by only recognising the international market value of shrimp.

The project's aim was to deliberately destroy the ecological models of shrimp farming and replace them with ecologically destructive practices. The staff appraisal report states, 'To date, almost all shrimp culture is based on a traditional, extensive shrimp culture system, with ponds frequently used for paddy cultivation in the rainy season and converted to shrimp and fish culture in the remaining period. As a result, shrimp yields are low, reflecting poor infrastructure, low density of stocking, inadequate or no water exchange, lack of feed and low level of technology.' [2]

The yield of shrimp quite clearly is not the only yield in traditional shrimp culture, which considers the yields of paddy and fresh water simultaneously with that of shrimp, thus conserving ecosystems while producing enough for human needs. In the state of Kerala such rotational cultivation of shrimp and paddy is called *Chemmeen Kutti* and *Pokkali*. The World Bank's philosophy, however, does not allow such conservation and need-based production to be considered 'productive': only that which increases exports and profits is 'productive', in this view.

The proposal to give market values to all resources as a solution to the ecological crisis is like offering the disease as the cure. This disease is reflected in the change in the meaning of the term 'resource' itself, which originally implied life. Its root is the Latin verb *surgere* which evoked the image of a spring that continually surges up from the ground. Natural regeneration, along with human reciprocation, were inherent in the traditional notion of 'resource'.

With the advent of industrialism and colonialism, however, a conceptual break occurred. 'Natural resources' became those raw materials of nature which were exploited for industrial production and colonial trade. With the capacity of regeneration gone, the attitude of reciprocity has also lost its ground: it is now simply human industry which 'impart value' to nature. For natural resources required to be 'developed'. Nature's capacity to renew itself had been denied. The economy of nature had been undermined by the economy of the market.

In a stable constellation of economic organisation, nature's economy is recognised as the most basic, in the sense that it is the base of the people's and market economies; however, development and economic growth treat the market economy as primary, neglecting nature's economy and the people's economy. Commodification of resources needs to be replaced by the recovery of commons which involves the reaffirmation of nature's economy; and this in turn calls for the restoration of the spiritual, ecological and social dimensions of nature.

Marketisation is based not only on the fallacy that 'value' equals 'price', but also on the myth that privatisation can help to preserve resources by preventing the over-exploitation that results from commonly held property resources. While commons are based on inalienability of shared rights derived from use, privatisation is based on tradeability of private property. The assumption that alienability is more conducive to conservation is derived from the false association of price with value.

Thus as Pearce and Warford argue, 'in the absence of rights to sell or transfer land, the land 'owner' may be unable to realise the value of any improvements and thus has little incentive to invest in long term measures such as soil conservation.' This assumption is patently false, since the best examples of soil conservation (for example, the hill terraces of the Himalaya) are realised precisely for the opposite reasons. Communities not threatened by alienation of resources and their benefits have a long term interest not only in conserving resources, but also in maximising benefit from them without compromising the viability of these resources.

Economic growth takes place through the over-exploitation of natural resources which creates a scarcity of natural resources in nature's economy and the survival economy. Further economic growth cannot help in the regeneration of the very spheres which must be destroyed if economic growth has to take place. Nature shrinks as capital. The growth of the market cannot solve the very crisis it creates. Further, while natural resources can be converted into cash, cash cannot be converted into nature's ecological processes. Those who offer market solutions to the ecological crisis limit themselves to the market, and look for substitutes to the commercial function of natural resources as commodities and raw material. However, in nature's economy, the currency is not money, it is life.

The neglect of the role of natural resources in ecological processes and in people's sustenance economy, and the diversion and destruction of these resources for commodity production and capital accumulation, are the main reasons for the ecological crisis and the crisis of survival in the Third World. The solution seems to lie in giving local communities control over local resources so that they have the rights and responsibility to rebuild nature's economy, and through it their sustenance.

We have called this recovery of the commons 'Aquarian Reform' in the context of the crisis of fisheries. As we stated in *Ecology and the Politics of Survival* [3] Aquarian Reforms have two facts:

1. Reserving the right to own fishing assets exclusively to those who are willing to fish themselves, no absentee 'sealords'.
2. Placing the primary right and responsibility for management of the marine resources at the micro and mezzo levels to such a working fishing community.

These reforms are mutually reinforcing and will restrict the tendency to enjoy short-term gains at the expense of a long-term crisis. They will ensure greater distributive justice, participation and sustainability.

[1] Ved Vyas, *Sri Vishnu Purana,* Geetha Press, Gorakhpur, January 1982

[2] 'The Aquaculture Disaster: Prawn Profits Pauperise Coastal India' in *The Ecologist Asia*, Vol. 3 no.5 September/October 1995

[3] Vandana Shiva, 'Ecology and the Politics of Survival: Conflicts over Natural Resources in India', Sage Publications, 1991, p.325

Chapter 5

Managing in an era of uncertainty

Introduction

Charles N Ehler

The world languishes and withers,
The heavens languish together with the earth,
The earth lies polluted under its inhabitants,
For they have transgressed the laws,
Violated the statutes, broken the everlasting covenant.

(Isaiah 24:4-5)

A major challenge today is managing human activities to achieve desirable goals, such as the sustainable use of coastal and marine resources, under conditions of scientific uncertainty, inherent variability of ecological and social systems and conflicting perceptions of problems and solutions. Few, if any, social institutions today are prepared to manage in a sustainable manner. Experience has taught us that both ecological and social systems are inherently more complex, more dynamic and unpredictable than we have previously imagined. We know that free markets acting alone cannot achieve socially desirable results since not all of the products and services of coastal and marine areas can be expressed in monetary terms. Institutional arrangements that recognise 'common stewardship' responsibilities must be found.

The papers in this chapter develop these ideas. Edward Goldsmith argues that large, single-purpose institutions such as the Food and Agriculture Organisation (FAO) of the United Nations and the World Bank cannot displace multi-purpose institutions such as families and local communities. He rightly points out that private interests working through the free market cannot ensure the stewardship of nature and cannot be a means of distributing resources in an equitable and sustainable manner. He asserts that localised, community-based economies are the only ones that can satisfy all human requirements on a sustainable basis. The principle that the protection of nature cannot be concerned only with the present, but must also care for the future, is outlined by Professor Alexandre Kiss. He reminds us that wealth inherited from previous generations should not be dissipated for our own convenience, but passed on to those who follow. Graeme Kelleher emphasises the importance of benefits to local communities and the generation of a sense of community ownership as a basis for establishing marine protected areas such as the Great Barrier Reef Marine Park. The importance of marine protected areas must be complemented by integrated management of the land and sea to ensure that human use is sustainable. Laurence Mee uses the Black Sea as a case study of a region suffering from catastrophic degradation of its environment and resources. However, he points out that over the past several years improved communications among institutions and stakeholders and integrated management actions have begun to bear fruit towards environmental restoration.

We live in frustrating times. Conflicts about how to achieve solutions to problems of sustainable use of resources abound. Mutual suspicions dominate; examples of co-operative approaches to common problems are few and far between. The result too often is ecosystem deterioration, economic stagnation and growing public mistrust. The challenge is to build institutional capacity at all levels of government, but particularly at the local level with the full involvement of all local interest groups. One solution lies in finding appropriate incentives that would compel private users of environmental resources to take into account the social costs of their actions. We need to re-evaluate continually the fundamental source of environmental problems, redirect policy towards environmental restoration and implement an adaptive process of planning and management that provides and acts on continually updated understanding. Above all, given the fundamental uncertainties about the nature of ecosystems and the possible consequences of poor decision making, it is necessary to act in a 'precautionary manner' that conserves and maintains environmental quality, both today and for future generations.

Institutions in Crisis

Edward Goldsmith

The key concepts that I wish to discuss in relation to this topic are: the management of human activities, the free market, the stewardship of nature and sustainable development.

The first thing one has to realise is that institutions have not been in existence for very long. Until quite recently, most of the functions that they fulfil were fulfilled by families and communities. Historically, we have moved from a world which consisted of families and communities living in loose societies to a world made up of institutions and corporations, and this has involved a massive change in everything that happens on our planet.

It is clear to me that by their very nature institutions have a number of failings. The first has been pointed out by Roy Rappaport, the anthropologist at Michigan university. He refers to them as single purpose organisations, whereas the families and communities they have supplanted are multi-purpose. When the latter undertook economic and other activities, they sought to satisfy a host of biological, religious, social and ecological requirements essential for maintaining their integrity and stability. In contrast institutions, by their very nature, are largely concerned with assuring their own immediate interests.

In the field of agriculture this can be illustrated by a consideration of rice growing in Sri Lanka and India. In the past around 400 varieties of rice were grown in Sri Lanka and about 30,000 varieties in India. Special varieties were considered suitable for different people and occasions, for example for pregnant women, men who worked in the fields, the clergy, special feasts and wet and dry climates. In other words, the aim of the rice producing communities was to satisfy a host of different, quite subtle requirements. Today, agriculture, controlled as it is by big companies that sell the inputs and by big companies (often the same ones) that buy the produce, process and market it, is geared specifically to cutting costs and increasing yields. As pressure to do this increases, the other varieties tend to disappear.

Another example of a community in which agriculture satisfies more than one purpose has been observed by Peter Huber, an anthropologist studying the Anggor tribe in New Guinea. He has pointed out that their agricultural system does not just produce food, it also produces social organisation. Maintaining the cohesion of their society is seen as being just as important as producing food.

The second problem with institutions is usually referred to as goal displacement. An institution may start off with the desire to solve a particular problem but all too easily it gets diverted. It finds that, in order to survive, it must increase its power and influence and this inevitably becomes its overriding goal. It has to adopt procedures and seek to achieve ends which are not always reconcilable with its original goal.

A typical example is the FAO, the Food and Agriculture Organisation of the United Nations, which I have looked at in some detail. Clearly the original goal of the FAO was to feed the world's population but at the moment its activities are probably helping us to do exactly the opposite. The FAO is funded by many different governments, which have very different priorities. They are much more interested in selling the inputs that their industries produce, such as fertilisers and pesticides, and helping their engineering companies to build dams and selling turbines for them. This means that the FAO is condemned to promoting high-input agriculture, which cannot feed the world.

This type of agriculture works against the FAO's aims in three ways. Firstly, where it is imposed, small farmers cannot afford it and are forced out of business and into the slums of the big cities. In India alone, maybe 20 million people are being forced into the slums as a result of development programmes which include agriculture and big irrigation schemes. Secondly, these countries are forced to export the food they produce because they must earn the foreign exchange with which to pay the interest on the loans that they have contracted in order to build the dams and the fertiliser factories, and to import the pesticides. Much of the good land in the countries that adopt this high-input agriculture is therefore used for exports, and there is very little land left for feeding local people. Although India is 'self sufficient' in food, 85 % of the children suffer from malnutrition because the people who are hungry do not have any money and cannot exert effective demand. Thirdly of course, the soil in the Third World usually has a lower organic content than it does in temperate areas and is subject to greater strain because the rains all come at once, so the soil is rapidly turned into dust as is happening in the Punjab and Haryana and other places where the Green Revolution promoted by the FAO has been adopted. All these things prevent the FAO from achieving its original goal, and it cannot do otherwise or it would not be allowed to exist.

Examples of goal displacement can be found in other institutions, for example the same thing happens with the World Bank which claims repeatedly that its main goal is to fight poverty in the Third World. In reality, to stay in office the World Bank must lend a great deal of money, 23 billion dollars, which is very difficult to do. This means that it must look for massive schemes, such as large dams, to support. Such massive schemes are almost always very destructive, both environmentally and socially. Moreover, the World Bank is 'procurement' driven, and is only tolerated by the Republicans who control Congress because it provides contracts for American industrialists who seek to expand their businesses into the Third World. Having to satisfy industry, chambers of commerce and the US Congress makes the World Bank's original goal very difficult to achieve. Goal displacement is very difficult for large institutions to avoid.

The third problem with institutions is that they tend to be dominated by transnational corporations which are becoming ever more powerful, especially now that we have ratified the Gatt Uruguay Round agreement and set up a global economy. Many of our institutions, such as the Ministry of Agriculture and Fisheries in Britain and the USDA in America, are largely dominated by the agro-chemical industry. The World Health Organisation is also now largely dominated by industry - in this case by the pharmaceutical industry, and the World Trade Organisation by transnationals of all sorts. These institutions, despite their initial goals, become committed to the policy that satisfies the priority of the transnational corporations, which is maximising trade and reducing costs on an increasingly global level, regardless of its consequences.

The fourth problem with institutions is that human activities are of a sort that cannot be managed by them. I see families and communities as 'natural' social groupings. We evolved as integral parts of families and communities, and it is only at the level of these social groupings that the activities required to maintain human survival can be properly fulfilled. Thus it is only the family that is remotely capable of properly bringing up our children and assuring the early stages of their education. The idea that an institution, however sophisticated, can replace the family is preposterous. Mr Newt Gingrich has said that children from one-parent families should be removed from their parent and consigned to an institution. This is like suggesting that the best thing to do with a man with only one leg is to remove that one too. It is also easy to show that the only device that has ever worked for controlling crime is the pressure of public opinion at the community level, reflecting traditional values and amply fed by malicious gossip, where everyone knows each other. Once the community has disintegrated, it is impossible to control crime and to maintain social order. I believe that in America there are now one and a half million people behind bars, but this has not made it any safer to walk the streets of the South Bronx or Detroit. Similarly, effective population control is only possible via strategies built into the cultural pattern of traditional societies and imposed at a community level. Once these communities disintegrate under the impact of development, institutions cannot replace them. Institutionalised family planning is largely irrelevant. I also believe that democratic government is only possible at the community level, that the human community, the *Gemeinschaft*, is the correct unit of democratic government. I do not believe that it is possible to have real democracy in an atomised and anonymous society, such as we have today.

These four fundamental problems with institutions tend to rule out, for me, the notion that they can ensure the stewardship of nature. To think that the atomised society of the modern world is capable of ensuring any sort of stewardship seems to me an even more utopian idea.

To those who believe that the establishment of a free market has created a level playing field for Third World countries, I would object that there are no such things as a free market or a level playing field. Forty to fifty per cent of the market for any of the major commodities, such as tea, coffee, sugar, cotton, aeroplanes and others is in the hands of five large companies, and with the GATT agreements now signed this can only increase. Anyone who wished to compete with these large corporations, which already control so much of the market, would have very little chance of winning. Moreover, access to the products sold on the market is only available to those who can exert effective demand for them, that is to say those whose needs are backed by hard cash. In fact, it could be said that the market is a device for transferring resources from those who have no money to those who do have money. Of course, future generations do not exert any effective demand, nor does the natural world, so the free market totally ignores the requirements of future generations, the natural world, and the world's poor. It cannot possibly be a means of distributing resources in an equitable and sustainable manner.

Finally, I do not believe that sustainable development is possible, I see it as a contradiction in terms. We cannot increase development any further, for it must mean increasing the impact of our activities on the environment, and the environment cannot even sustain the present impact. We need to develop a sustainable society which does not involve increasing this impact, which means a society which has much in common with the traditional societies of old, one whose religion, among other things, was embedded in society, in the natural world and in the cosmos itself, and thereby served to sanctify their critical structure. Such a society, of course, must be made up of families organised into largely autonomous communities and its economy must be embedded with these key social units, catering for a relatively local market. One of our challenges today is to recreate local economies of this sort, which are the only ones that could possibly satisfy all our social, ecological and, indeed, economic requirements in a sustainable manner.

Marine Protected Areas

Graeme Kelleher

> No man is an island,
> Entire of itself.
> Every man is a piece of the continent, a part of the main ...
> And therefore never send to know
> for whom the bell tolls.
> It tolls for thee.
>
> (John Donne, Meditation XVII, 17th Century)

There is a positive message in this quotation, which reflects the essence of this symposium. The future of the world depends on individuals, acting alone or in concert with others.

As Vice-Chairman, Marine of IUCN's Commission on National Parks and Protected Areas (CNPPA), in 1990 I established 18 Working Groups of scientists and managers, one group for each of the major biogeographical regions of the world.

Together, these regions cover the full range of coastal marine zones:

- tropical ecosystems including coral reefs;
- temperate zones;
- the Arctic and Antarctic.

The task of the Working Groups was to identify priorities for establishing Marine Protected Areas (MPAs) or for developing effective management in existing 'paper parks'. The aims of MPAs are to protect the natural environment, particularly its biodiversity and biological productivity, and to provide for ecologically sustainable use of the marine coastal environment, particularly by adjacent coastal communities.

Some financial and other support for this very large task was provided by the World Bank and the Great Barrier Reef Marine Park Authority, but the great majority of the work was done by individuals working voluntarily without financial recompense.

The work has been completed and the four-volume report was published in June 1995 in Washington DC, with financial assistance from the Dutch Government, for which we are most grateful. Copies of the report may be obtained from the IUCN, the Environment Division of the World Bank or the Great Barrier Reef Marine Park Authority.

Some features of this project echo the principles identified in the debate on Revelation and the Environment. The criteria used in selecting the priority areas focused on practicality - we were not interested in making recommendations that would never be implemented - therefore the social and political feasibility of carrying out each recommendation was given great weight. One of the most important determinants of social feasibility was the existence of potential benefit to local communities from the creation of the MPA. That is to say, the interdependence of nature and humanity was overtly recognised. In addition, priorities were identified by scientists and managers working together. This approach, which had rarely been used previously in any of the regions, recognised that intellectual links between different fields of human activity must be established. We now have a Report which identifies all the existing MPAs in the world as well as the regional and national priorities for further action.

We are taking advantage of regional meetings being organised by bodies such as UNEP, the International Coral Reef Initiative and CNPPA, to develop specific proposals for funding from sources such as the Global Environment Facility, the World Bank, regional banks, UNDP, national aid organisations and private sources.

There is much reason for optimism. The almost universal recognition of the threats to the global environment is a necessary foundation on which to build a real sense of stewardship in human communities. Events such as the coming into effect of the UN Convention on the Law of the Sea and the Convention on Biological Diversity show that such a sense is developing, not only in relation to the land, but to the sea as well.

It is my hope that there will be increased support for the implementation of the recommendations in this Report, which are practical steps to help humanity live in harmony with nature. MPAs can be a major contributor to the aims of this debate, but not in isolation. They must be complemented by integrated management of land and sea to ensure that human use is sustainable.

Such overall integrated management of land and sea is the ultimate aim but large MPAs are a useful first step. Let us look briefly at one example of an MPA - the Great Barrier Reef Marine Park - and identify the general lessons that can be learned from that experience.

The Great Barrier Reef Marine Park covers an area larger than that of the UK or Greece. It supports economic activity worth more than $1 billion per annum, including commercial and recreational fishing, tourism and shipping. It is not a single reef - it contains 2,9,00 individual reefs and 918 islands. It is one of the most biologically diverse environments on earth, supporting more than 400 species of coral and 1,500 species of fish. It is managed by an Authority, with the goal 'to provide for the protection, wise use, understanding and enjoyment of the Great Barrier Reef in perpetuity '.

This goal, slightly reworded, has been adopted by the IUCN (the International Union for the Conservation of Nature):

> to provide for the protection, restoration, wise use, understanding and enjoyment of the marine heritage of the world in perpetuity, through the creation of a global, representative system of marine protected areas and through the management, in accordance with the principles of the World Conservation Strategy, of human activities that use or affect the marine environment.

The words I would particularly like to stress are 'in perpetuity'. They place a measurable obligation on the management authority to prevent insidious and progressive deterioration in any environmental qualities. The agency must define the threats to the environment and devise and apply procedures to control them.

In order to define and control the threats, the agency must:

- measure the current state of each environmental indicator, such as water quality;

- measure the effects of human activity by a formal monitoring programme. This identifies the trends in environmental quality;

- define what changes in human activity are needed to maintain environmental quality;

and

- convince the community that the changes in human activity must occur.

Perhaps this last step is the most difficult, but the solution to it can be applied generally to natural resource management. It can be summarised as generating a sense of community ownership and, consequently, stewardship.

In the case of water quality, for example, the major threat to the Great Barrier Reef derives from run-off from the mainland agricultural areas. The problem is mainly nutrients - nitrogen and phosphorus - which are applied to the land as fertiliser. In order to generate a sense of ownership in the farming community, we emphasise common interests - the farmers don't like their expensive fertiliser to leave the farm and we don't like the fertiliser to reach the sea. Therefore, we involve the industry in the design, conduct and interpretation of the research and monitoring programmes. In this way we become colleagues rather than enemies. The farmers become convinced of the validity of the research and monitoring conclusions and tend to support the management actions which flow from them. In short, they develop a sense of ownership of both the resources and the management system.

This principle of generating community ownership is applied to all facets of the Marine

Park. The major control mechanism within the park is zoning. The human activities which are permitted in each zone are carefully defined. The degree of restriction in the zones varies from few restrictions in general use zones to complete prohibition of almost all human activities in preservation zones.

Again, the essence of this strategy is to develop a sense of ownership of the zoning plan within the community. This is achieved by deliberately carrying out, in the preparation of the zoning plan, the most comprehensive public involvement programme anywhere in the world. Perhaps it could be called agreement by exhaustion!

At the end of the process the general community, as well as all the individual user groups, have a sense that they have been given every opportunity to contribute and that the plan represents as good a compromise between competing objectives as can be achieved in practice.

Two comments need to be made to qualify this description of the process. First, although the process is extremely democratic, hard decisions are taken when scientific information shows that they are necessary to achieve the primary goal. The second comment flows from the first - inevitably there are occasions when decisions are taken which are opposed by one or more interested groups.

I have described briefly a few approaches which have been adopted in the Great Barrier Reef because I believe that they exemplify principles which are applicable anywhere. In particular, they illustrate the overriding importance of generating a sense of community ownership in any natural resource management system.

I believe that large, multiple use Marine Protected Areas, preferably covering complete ecosystems, are an effective tool for achieving the dual aims encapsulated in the phrase 'ecologically sustainable development'. These aims are to protect ecological processes and states, and to provide for sustainable human use of the sea and its resources.

It is my hope that the international community will support the creation of a global, representative system of Marine Protected Areas, using the principle of community ownership as the organising force. This could make an important contribution towards achievement of ecologically sustainable human use of both the land and the sea.

Legal Dimensions of Common Stewardship

Alexandre Kiss

The Book of Revelation illuminates two important concepts characterising the relationship between humans and the environment which can be seen to be relevant to environmental law.

The first is the unity of the world or of what we now call the biosphere. Chapter 10, verses 2, 5 and 8 present the image of:

> Another mighty angel come down from heaven ... he set his right foot upon the sea, and his left foot on the earth.

The image of the unity of the sea and earth is complemented by the unity of the whole creation. Chapter 5 verse 13 gives a beautiful representation of this:

> And every creature which is in heaven, and on the earth, and under the earth, and such as are in the sea, and all that are in them, heard I saying: Blessing, and honour, and glory and power, be unto him that sitteth upon the throne, and unto the Lamb for ever and ever.

The second important teaching of Revelation is the responsibility of humankind. In Chapter 11 the seventh angel sounds his trumpet announcing the judgement:

> 16. And the four and twenty elders, which sat before God on their seats, fell upon their faces, and worshipped God.
>
> 17. Saying, We give thee thanks, O Lord God Almighty ... because thou hast taken to thee thy great power, and hast reigned.
>
> 18. And the nations were angry, and thy wrath is come, and the time of the dead, that they should be judged, and that thou shouldest give reward unto thy servants the prophets, and to the saints, and them that fear thy name, small and great; and shouldest destroy them which destroy the earth.

The wretched are punished by the destruction of what today we would call natural resources and life-support systems: the sea (Chapter 8:8-9, 16:3), the earth (Chapter 6:12-14; 7:1-3; 8:7; 11:6; 16:2, 18, 20), the rivers (Chapter 8:10-11; 16:4, 12) and even the sun and the stars (Chapter 6:12-13; 8:12; 16:8). These texts implicitly stress the unity of the whole creation.

How can law, particularly international law, build on these two concepts? As a first step we must consider the nature of law.

It is generally agreed that one of the main functions of every legal system, whether national, regional or world-wide, is to reveal, recognise and incarnate the basic values of the society concerned. Thus, throughout history it has been recognised that human life is of value and should be protected by punishing those who attempt to extinguish it; that fundamental human rights and freedoms are precious and should be protected; that social justice must be accepted as a goal and appropriate measures to achieve it should be taken at national as well as international levels. The legal system did not create these values; they emerged gradually from the religious, ethical and cultural foundations of societies. The legal system brought these values into the open by discussing them, recognising them and then taking appropriate measures to protect them by the only means at its disposal. Within states this process is characterised by the inclusion of principles enshrining these values in constitutions or constitutional texts, which have to be implemented by specific legislation. In the international sphere the values are often formulated and enshrined in non-binding declarations (such as the Universal Declaration of Human Rights), the principles of which are later transformed into obligatory statutes by inserting them into treaties.

This pattern was followed for the environment. Through scientific knowledge and the general understanding that natural resources are being depleted and even clean water and air are becoming scarce in certain areas, we have become much more aware of the value of the environment. We are beginning to recognise our responsibilities as human beings towards one another and towards the rest of the planet, and to realise that society must value and protect the environment.

This, described in a very simplified way, is the origin of environmental law. However, this new branch of legal science - and national and international legislation - presents several characteristics which do not naturally fit into jurisprudence. One of these is the temporal dimension which is a fundamental element of environmental protection. It is often considered that law has the function of assuring a certain social stability and, as a consequence, it must focus on safeguarding present situations. Environmental protection requires a constant adaptation of the statutes to changing circumstances, including new discoveries and new forms of depletion of the biosphere.

In addition, the protection of Nature and its resources cannot be concerned exclusively with the present. The very idea of conservation implies a temporal dimension, a care for the future. A conscious decision to abstain from exhausting the world's natural resources, instead of enjoying to the maximum the possibilities which they present us with today, necessarily involves thinking about the future.

The first step in this direction is the requirement that deterioration of the environment should be prevented and therefore foreseen and assessed. An advanced form of prevention was developed in international environmental law, in the precautionary principle:

> Where there are threats of serious or irreversible damage, lack of full scientific certainty shall not be used as a reason for postponing cost-effective measures to prevent environmental degradation. (Rio Declaration of June 1992, principle 15)

Such a principle implies the necessity to identify scientific uncertainty and to predict serious or irreversible damage. The latter clearly has a temporal element which can lead us somewhat beyond the traditional legal concepts of liability and even of responsibility.

The temporal dimension of environmental law is even more apparent in the principle of the rights of future generations, which emerged alongside realisation of the need to protect the environment. According to Principle 1 of the 1972 Stockholm Declaration on the Human Environment:

> Man ... bears a solemn responsibility to protect and improve the environment for present and future generations.

The same principle has been re-affirmed by numerous international treaties and other instruments.

The rights of future generations are rooted in psychological and ethical factors. All living species instinctively seek to ensure their own reproduction, and the more developed of them make provision for the future welfare of their descendants. Human history testifies that the instinct to care for children, and for their children in turn, is a part of human nature. Ethical considerations dictate that, for the sake of fairness, the wealth which we have inherited from previous generations should not be dissipated for our own convenience and pleasure, but passed on, in as great a measure as possible, to those who follow us. The term 'intergenerational equity' has been used to convey this concept.

However, the concept of 'future generations' is difficult to define. It certainly does not imply that when a new generation appears the existing one disappears. Every second hundreds of human beings are born and die and more than five billion people of all ages co-exist at present. It would be more accurate to speak not of generations but of a constant flow: humanity can be compared with a huge river which flows ceaselessly, becoming ever larger, and in which no distinction can be made between the drops of water which make it up.

The logical consequence of such an approach would be to recognise humankind, in the present and the future, as the guardian of rights. In principle this understanding could be recognised under international law. It implies the individual responsibility of every person for safeguarding the environment in the present and passing it on to future humanity.

It must be added that since the middle of the 1980s we have known that safeguarding the environment requires global approaches. We are reminded again of the Book of Revelation, which proclaims the unity of the universe. As a consequence, individual responsibility must be concerned with the protection of the global environment, by all appropriate means. The World Charter for Nature, adopted and solemnly proclaimed by the UN General Assembly on 28 October 1982, states that each person has a duty to act in accordance with its provisions, acting individually, in association with others or through participation in the political process (UN General Assembly Resolution 37/3, principle 24).

However, environmental law cannot restrict itself to proclaiming principles. It must also establish appropriate legal procedures through which the representation of the rights and interests of humankind can be ensured.

In relation to this, in 1989 the establishment of a Commission on the Future of the Planet was proposed (E Brown Weiss, *In Fairness to Future Generations: International Law, Common Patrimony and Intergenerational Equity*, p.148-152). Unfortunately the 1992 Rio Conference failed to get involved in such considerations and the bodies which were created were either inappropriate or powerless.

Considering the serious warning in the Book of Revelation concerning the destruction of the environment by humans, one could imagine that the 24 elders of the Apocalypse - perhaps significant in being twice the number of the tribes of Israel or of the number of the disciples - might represent the world's population.

It has been proposed several times to set up an independent body, the composition of which could make one think of the elders 'clothed in white raiment' in Revelation, Chapter 4:4 - perhaps a reference to their very high moral status! Although its role should not be to judge the governments of different countries, but to invite them in specific cases to think and to act for the long term, such a proposal is not likely to be accepted during the coming years by sovereign states, which dislike any intervention in their policies. Nevertheless, the Book of Revelation is very clear on the responsibility of those 'which destroy the earth' (Chapter 11:18). One of the prophetic tasks of the world religions could be to remind them of their responsibility.

Can the Black Sea be Saved?

Laurence D Mee

The Black Sea: a unique environment

Almost one third of the entire land area of continental Europe drains into the Black Sea. It is an area which includes major parts of seventeen countries, thirteen capital cities and some 160 million persons. The second, third and fourth major European rivers, the Danube, Dnieper and Don, discharge into this sea but its only connection to the world's oceans is the narrow Bosphorus Channel. The Bosphorus is as little as 70 metres deep and 700 metres wide but the depth of the Black Sea itself exceeds two kilometres in places.

The large natural river supply of phosphorus and nitrogen, essential nutrients for marine plants and algae, has always made the Black Sea very fertile. The tiny floating marine plants known as phytoplankton which form the base of the marine food chain are either eaten or die and gradually fall to deeper waters where bacteria take care of decomposing them, almost completely. Replenishment of the bottom waters of the sea with new seawater from the Mediterranean takes hundreds of years. The bacteria in the bottom waters quickly consume all the oxygen and the sea is virtually dead below a depth of about 180 metres. The Black Sea is the biggest natural anoxic basin the world. Despite this situation, for millennia, its surface waters supported a rich and diverse marine life. Its coastal inhabitants prospered from the abundant fisheries and, more recently, from the millions of tourists who come to bathe in its warm waters and enjoy the beauty of its shorelines, plains and mountains.

The Black Sea in crisis

In a period of only three decades, the Black Sea has suffered the catastrophic degradation of a major part of its natural resources. Increased loads of nutrients from rivers caused an overproduction of tiny phytoplankton which in turn blocked the light reaching the sea grasses and algae, essential components of the sensitive ecosystem of the north-western shelf. The entire ecosystem began to collapse. This problem, coupled with pollution and irrational exploitation of fish stocks, set off a sharp decline in fisheries resources. To make matters worse, in the mid-1980s, a jellyfish-like species *(Mnemiopsis leidyi)*, invaded the Black Sea, having been brought in accidentally by a ship's ballast water from America's eastern seaboard; it quickly reached a total mass of 900 million tons (ten times the annual fish harvest from the entire world). Though declining, *Mnemiopsis* continues to plague the Black Sea.

Poor planning, uncontrolled sewage pollution, direct dumping, tanker accidents - all this has resulted not just in ugliness and environmental damage, but also in numerous beach closures and considerable losses in the tourist industry. This came at a time when five of the Black Sea countries were facing social and economic upheavals and were unable to take the necessary remedial actions.

The exploitation of the Black Sea's resources in the past few decades has clearly been unsustainable. The environment of the Black Sea has deteriorated dramatically in terms of its biodiversity, habitats, fisheries resources, aesthetic and recreational value and water quality. The Black Sea has many 'uses', ranging from fishing, tourism and mineral extraction on the one hand, to its use as a cheap transport route and as a convenient place to dump solid and liquid waste on the other. Many of these uses have an additional economic cost through their impact on the environment. The present environmental crisis has been precipitated largely by ignoring these hidden costs; by paying little or no attention to these 'costs', they have been conveniently transferred from one generation to the next. Here, environmental and ethical issues are juxtaposed. Is it right to promote rapid economic growth whilst transferring part of the cost to the next generation? Clearly some of the benefits of growth are also transferred, but what about the costs of military and other activities of questionable social benefit?

The need for international action

The resources of the Black Sea - and its problems - are shared by six coastal countries, Bulgaria, Georgia, Romania, Russia, Turkey and Ukraine. Management of the Black Sea's shared resources is the responsibility of these countries but part of the responsibility for controlling aquatic and airborne pollution should also be shared amongst the other eleven countries which have a major part of their territory in the Black Sea basin. Protection of the Black Sea cannot be achieved on a unilateral basis. Almost every use of the sea and coastal areas has the potential for affecting the well-being of neighbouring countries. Even pollution restricted to the vicinity of an industrial plant may affect the economic development of another country by killing juvenile fish which would have otherwise migrated to its coastal seas. On the other hand, countries may wish to overexploit their part of a migrating resource in order to deny access (and advantage) to the neighbours. Through joint management and harmonised policy objectives, a collective sense of ownership of the Sea's resources can be attained : 'owners' tend to protect their property more than those enjoying a free service. The goals were clear to all: what was needed was an effective international strategy.

A strategy develops ... and the Black Sea environmental program is born

The first move was to establish a new legal framework for co-operation. Inspired by the Regional Seas Conventions which emerged after the 1972 Stockholm Conference on Environment and Development, representatives of the Black Sea countries drafted and signed, in April 1992, their own 'Convention for the Protection of the Black Sea Against Pollution'; it consisted in a basic framework of agreement and three specific Protocols on pollution from different sources - dumping, land-based pollutants and accidents.

The Convention was followed up by a Ministerial Declaration on the Protection of the Black Sea Environment; duly signed by all six Ministers of the Environment in Odessa in April 1993, this innovative document set the stage for three years of change.

The Black Sea countries requested support from the Global Environment Facility, GEF, a US$ 2 billion fund established in 1991 under the management of the World Bank, the UN Development Programme and the UN Environmental Programme. In June 1993, a three year Black Sea Environmental Programme was established with US$ 9.3 million funding from GEF and collateral funding from other industrialised countries: the BSEP was born.

The Black Sea Environmental Program

Although most Black Sea countries had a considerable number of dedicated experts, the linkage between their work and national and regional decision-making on environmental matters was often poor. National environmental legislation was often based upon unenforceable objectives or lacked effective economic instruments such as fines or permit charges. As a result of years of isolation, many institutions lacked the modern means of providing reliable information on the state of the environment itself: such information being the cornerstone for improving environmental policy.

These realities were addressed at the first meeting of the Black Sea Environmental Programme (BSEP) Steering Committee which took place in Varna, Bulgaria, in June 1993. The meeting, which brought together government representatives, GEF partners and representatives of Non Governmental Organisations (NGOs), selected three overall BSEP objectives in the context of a three-year plan: to improve the capacity of Black Sea countries to assess and manage the environment; to support the development and implementation of new environmental policies and laws; and to facilitate the preparation of sound environmental investments. The first BSEP challenge was to rebuild institutional linkages in a region which was not only undergoing a socio-economic crisis, but also frequently lacked modern means of communication.

A system of thematic Working Parties has been established, based upon regional 'Activity Centres'. Each Black Sea country agreed to host one of these Centres and corresponding National Focal Points were established for each Centre in each of the other countries (see illustrations). For overall co-ordination, a Programme Co-ordinating Unit (PCU) was established in Istanbul on 2 January, 1994; this works directly with the

National Co-ordinators, high level government officials appointed by the Ministers of Environment. The PCU has a small expert staff which deals with all issues relevant to environmental management.

For their part, the NGOs are very active in programme implementation, have organised national and regional NGO fora for the Black Sea and select two representatives as observers to the BSEP Steering Committee. The entire BSEP network has been linked by electronic mail, a cost effective and reliable communications tool.

BSEP has developed a close relationship with other partners and organisations with similar goals, such as the Black Sea Economic Co-operation, the NATO Science for Stability Programme, specialised UN Agencies and International NGOs. The World Bank plays a particularly important financially supportive role, in close co-operation with the PCU.

What has been achieved?

Establishing and operating a network linking over 40 institutions around the Black Sea has proven a difficult but rewarding task. Some 23 thematic Working Party meetings have been held; fewer meetings will be necessary now, with the successful installation of the electronic mail network.

By the end of 1995, over 800 experts were mobilised in over 60 workshops, meetings and training sessions under the auspices of the BSEP. The BSEP has also contributed more than $1.5 million to re-equipping its pollution monitoring network. In order to increase public awareness, BSEP has recruited the support of NGOs as well as producing its own popular newsletters, films and posters.

Since effective environmental policy requires accurate and accessible information, each BSEP working party is preparing national and regional thematic reports. Together with the Black Sea Data System and the Black Sea Geographic Information System, these should ensure the ready availability of information and analysis to scientists, managers and national and regional-level policy makers.

Finally, the BSEP's environmental investment programme, led by the World Bank, has supported the development of an Urgent Investment Portfolio, which has already led to a US$ 18 million emergency concessionary loan to Georgia.

What will be done next?

At the governments' request, the BSEP will assist with the preparation of a strategic Black Sea Action Plan during 1996; the Plan will need to be a pragmatic statement of common ends and means. To ensure that the Black Sea Action Plan, along with the Bucharest Convention, do not fail to be implemented because of a lack of funding, the

BSEP is helping governments develop innovative mechanisms for financing environmental protection, such as a possible 'Black Sea Environmental Fund', which could be financed by such sources as transportation levies, tourist user fees and pollution charges.

Another future work area will involve the development of co-ordinated approaches to management of the major river basins - such as the Danube, Don, and Diner - feeding into the Black Sea. Integrating this work with a strategy for managing the Black Sea itself will remain a priority for action in the years ahead.

Towards a sustainable future

The Black Sea Action Plan, once adopted by the six coastal countries, together with the Bucharest Convention, will form a comprehensive framework for sustainable regional management. Governments will have to give priority to implementing and enforcing existing laws and policies; urgent investments will be required; a joint commitment to reducing pollution and over-exploitation of the biological and aesthetic resources must be affirmed. A co-ordinated contribution from the international community is needed; and local communities will also need to see for themselves how their efforts can contribute to a better future. Only in this way will the Black Sea be able to serve as the keystone of the sustainable development of the surrounding coastal economies. Sharing responsibility is more difficult than exchanging blame. Yet with a concerted effort, the beauty and richness of the Black Sea can be enjoyed by present and future generations alike.

Chapter 6

Defining what is possible

Introduction

Christos Yannaras

We are not an ecological or inter-faith conference of a general nature for the protection of the environment. The point of reference for our discussions and attempts to find solutions for problems is a particular text of the Christian Bible, the Revelation to John - a text of a religious tradition that has endowed the foundations of our modern Western European culture, the culture of the pollution and destruction of the environment, with its conceptual structure.

The theme of this part of our conference in particular is the exploration of the options available to us for the protection of the environment. Our options are not unrelated to the review of certain mistakes which have taken place in our culture, mistakes which originate in a particular reading and interpretation of the Revelation to John. We all agree that technical and organisational efforts to bring about a cessation of the destruction which our culture imposes on nature are not enough. It is, to say the least, contradictory that we should wish to correct our faults with the same logic and the same means that brought about these faults in the first place.

A different use of nature from that which is prevalent today presupposes a different view of nature, a different conception and interpretation of nature. Our ecological concern would be superficial if it were not founded on a different cosmology and approach to the world than that which prevails today. It is not within the powers of this symposium to change the attitude of governments or of industries, to impose a different way of controlling the renunciation or use of natural means.

I think that we should concentrate our attention on a proposal for a way of conceiving the world and of using the world. Such a proposal should have the capacity to lead progressively to new attitudes, to illuminate the destruction of the environment in analogy with the vandalisation of a work of art, of a thing made that preserves its uniqueness on account of its maker.

And in the formulation of such a proposal the text of the Revelation to John can function in a revelatory way.

Industry and the Environment

Rahmi M Koc

Over the last two decades the world has been torn between two basic philosophies that have been pulling in different directions. One was to achieve economic growth and the other was to protect the environment. During this period environmentalists all over the world increased their pressure on governments to introduce more stringent regulations to curb industrial pollution, to such an extent that development was hindered. This caused the business world to unite under a new concept called sustainable development, which aimed to maintain economic growth while protecting the environment. The World Conference on the Environment in Rio was the turning point where each side declared that they recognised and respected the other's views.

Economic growth in the world is the only key to maintaining and raising standards of living, improving the quality of people's lives and accumulating wealth. This can only be achieved through industrialisation, technological advances and free trade, which are closely linked to each other. Only business that is financially sound can increase investment and research, pay dividends and taxes, and create jobs.

Economic development does not preclude the protection of the environment; in fact it can provide a basis for it. Societies with stronger economies have sufficient resources to invest in producing a cleaner, safer environment and can afford to be more conservation conscious than less developed countries.

The treatment of waste water by different countries can illustrate this point for us. Sweden treats all of its waste water before it is discharged. America treats 97% of its waste water. In the case of Greece and Turkey, the figure is a mere 3-4%. In other words, in the less industrially developed, eastern European countries, only a small percentage of all waste water being discharged is treated. Moreover, because of their strong economic position, industrialised western nations have practically solved their own air pollution problems and can now turn to and invest in the former eastern European nations to rid them of their terrible air pollution.

From these examples it can be seen that any laws and regulations which hinder or prevent economic growth, in favour of extreme environmental concerns that are not based on scientific data, may work to the detriment of the environment. On the other hand, the business world, especially industry, should not turn a deaf ear to environmental concerns. Throughout every stage of the production process, from the extraction of raw materials to the product reaching the customer, and including the packaging process, businesses should adopt environmentally friendly procedures.

I believe that the time has come when both the environmentalists and the business world, instead of opposing each other, should work together, sitting down and ironing out their differences and trying to reach mutually beneficial solutions to the problem. Constant disagreements, clashes and stubbornness will help neither party.

In a world where globalisation is becoming not only fashionable but obligatory, concern for environmental issues can sometimes put a country in a disadvantageous position. In this respect, it is important that all countries play their part in creating a level playing field and that no unfair competition takes place. Sometimes, even within the same nation, we find some regions that act on environmental concerns and others that do not seem to care at all. This raises the question of countries being given the opportunity to adjust to environmental rules and regulations. Less developed nations should be granted a longer time frame as they will have more changes to cope with.

Let us take Turkey as an example. We have had to squeeze into 30-40 years what the western industrial world did in 200 or more years. When you try to turn a closed and backward agricultural society into an open, semi-industrialised one in such a short period, the environment comes fairly low on the list of priorities. The result of this was unbalanced development. Population growth, misuse of national resources and unplanned urban development have caused severe environmental damage. In other words, the environment was sacrificed for economic growth.

The first serious regulating check on the environment came with the passing of an environmental law in 1983. Regulations and acts that defined this law came into being much later. Because of this late awakening to the damage done to the environment, Turkey today is facing a severe pollution problem. Domestic pollution has been aggravated by pollution caused by outside factors which were beyond our control. The Black Sea has been polluted by tons of industrial chemical waste flowing in each day from the Danube, Don and Dinyeper rivers. Contaminated barrels discharged from foreign shipping and marine accidents have also added to the pollution. Nuclear residue from Chernobyl contaminated both sea and land species and, as a result of this, the 125 species of fish that existed in the 1970's have been reduced to only 3 or 4 species today. In fast developing urban areas, clean air is almost non-existent due to low quality coal and heavy oil. Leadless gasoline production is, at best, still marginal. We still have a population growth rate of 2.2% annually with big city population growth as high as 7%. Istanbul has become a megalopolis of more than 10 million people stretching over 100km and is impossible to manage.

The Koc Group declared war on industrial environmental pollution as early as 1985. We were the first company to set up a fully equipped and specialised environmental engineering department, at the Koc holding headquarters. The mission of this department is to fulfil Koc top management commitments for the protection of the environment.

This department sees to it that each and every production facility that belongs to the group complies with Turkish and EC environmental regulations on waste water treatment, air pollution, noise and solid waste control. After 10 years of hard work and millions of dollars of expenditure, we are finally content, satisfied that we are doing our duty to our nation and to the environment.

We periodically check the quality of the water we discharge, the noise levels, the smokeless stacks and so on. International amendments and issues relevant to each area of concern are closely monitored and regular adjustments in our practices are made. Of course, this puts us at a disadvantage in comparison with other industries that do not fully comply with the regulations. To compete on equal terms we have to work more efficiently, make better forecasts and be more alert. We are also constantly advising other companies, based on our experience in this field, and we give them free help and guidance if necessary.

This year's IFC annual report states for the Koc Group that 'overall environmental and occupational health and safety performance was equal to or better than in most companies in Europe'.

Thus, from an environmental point of view, we believe we are practising what has been declared in our 'Vision and Values Statement' by our founder Mr Vehbi Koc, which is implemented by all the employees of the Group: 'Creation of value, elimination of waste and efficient utilisation of all resources are our key objectives.'

The Role and Responsibility of the Media

Geoffrey Lean

Journalists, as a rule, intensely dislike discussing the 'role and responsibility of the media'. One reason is that journalism is, in many ways, essentially an irresponsible profession - in the strictest and least pejorative sense of the word. Like much of academia, it attracts people who prefer saying what should be done than actually putting it into practice. Nikita Kruschev, responding to western media criticism of his governance of the then Soviet Union, once said that it was easier to write a newspaper column than to run a country.

Another reason for this allergy comes from a reaction to hypocrisy. Journalism should be an attempt to find and communicate the truth, without regard to special interests. You would be amazed to find how often the promotion of a special interest is couched in terms of the 'responsibility' of a journalist or a newspaper to cover a particular subject or espouse a particular line.

No honest journalist - allergic to the concept or not - can deny, however, that his or her work carries huge responsibilities and plays an important role in the communication of information and ideas. Journalism helps set the political and policy agenda and affects the public mood. It has the power both to speak directly to the public over the heads of national leaders and to represent the concerns of the people to those leaders.

This can be particularly true over environmental issues, where there seems to be a strange lack of connection between leaders and the led. I was struck by a comment by Tim Wirth that the US Administration would have liked to have set stricter targets for the reduction of greenhouse gases, but did not have the necessary public constituency or votes in Congress. Indeed, the Clinton Administration did try, early on, to introduce an energy tax only to fail to attract much public support - even from environmental groups - and only to run into overwhelming congressional opposition; and that was when the Democrats still had a majority in both Houses and before the mid-term elections brought an influx of Republicans determined to dismantle the environmental measures of the last twenty years.

Yet the exit polls of that same mid-term election that swept the Republicans to their congressional majorities found that 83% of voters described themselves as 'environmentalists'. Indeed it was no accident that they did not include their plans on the environment in their *Contract with America*: polls had shown that these were very unpopular. Bill Reilly, Administrator of the Environmental Protection Agency under George Bush, told me just before the last Presidential Election how the Republicans' own pollsters had reported that environmental concerns 'had entered the core values of the American people, even in recession'. I remember too how public opinion forced President Bush into a more environmentally-friendly stance than he had planned at the Earth Summit in Rio in 1992.

It is much the same in Britain. Pollsters regularly find 80-90% support for environmental propositions. Even more interestingly, a MORI poll which measures what people actually do, rather than what they say, regularly finds that about a third of Britons are 'environmental activists'. Well over four million people belong to environmental pressure groups, the kind of membership numbers that political parties would kill for, yet neither of the big parties appear to have made any serious attempt either to meet these concerns, or, perhaps more surprisingly, to mobilise this latent political force.

Robin Cook, our shadow Foreign Secretary, has called environmental concerns 'the sleeping giant of British politics'. Every so often the giant turns over in his sleep, causing tremors throughout the political landscape, but soon appears to nod off again. One such episode occurred at the end of the 1980s when seals were found to be dying in the North Sea. There was immense public alarm, newspapers far from notable for their environmental concerns took up the cry, and it played a major part in Mrs Thatcher's celebrated 'green conversion' in 1989. Similarly Shell's plans to dump the Brent Spar oil platform in the sea earlier this year ran into such huge and vocal public protest throughout Europe that it had abruptly to abandon them.

It is as if there were a great oil-bearing strata of environmental concern under the normal ground of public and political life, and as if every so often someone, or some issue, succeeds in drilling down into it, bringing it gushing out onto the surface and taking everyone by surprise. The media have undoubtedly played a part both in creating the environmental consciousness that permeates the strata and in helping to power the drill that every so often taps into it - not by forethought or planning, but simply by reporting what is going on.

I got into this field, by accident, twenty-five years ago, in 1970, European Conservation Year. I had just started work on my first big newspaper, the *Yorkshire Post*. The editor decided that someone should be in charge of covering the Year, and as I was a new face, with no other responsibilities, I was volunteered. I soon became hooked, particularly as I came to realise that the environment was not primarily about tigers or toxic waste or even global warming or nuclear accidents, but about the well-being of people, now and in the future.

I was by no means the first newspaper environment correspondent in Britain but I have been the longest serving. A strong, if small, corps of environmental specialists in the late 1960s and early 1970s was dismantled as newspapers ceased to give much attention to the subject and it was not until the late 1980s that editors began appointing them again in any numbers. There is now a strong group again, if somewhat smaller than at its height at the turn of the decade, but for many years I used to meet the entire British national newspaper environment press corps every morning, in the shaving mirror.

It has been a privilege to be able to help define a new journalistic speciality but it has also been something of a struggle, for me and for others. The struggle has been not to push a particular point of view - that, emphatically, is not our job - but to get the environment taken seriously as a subject meriting proper coverage.

For many years, newspaper executives in Britain did not consider covering the environment to be real journalism - an attitude that still persists even on some 'serious' papers. It was, and often still is, thought to be a 'worthy' subject - the kiss of death in a newsroom. There are, I understand, similar attitudes in newspapers in many other countries.

Part of the problem stems from basic constraints in the way the media operates. We are very good at covering *events*, for example, but rather poor at reporting *processes*. So we can handle a Chernobyl or an Exxon Valdez quite well, even though we may not have been very good at exploring the underlying issues that led to both accidents, certainly not in advance. But we are very poor at reporting such ongoing, important processes as desertification, deforestation, or even climate change.

We are much better at presenting *images* than *arguments,* even in the written media. It often takes an image to bring an environmental issue alive. The Antarctic ozone hole - something people felt that they could easily envisage - was the catalyst that sparked coverage of ozone depletion. Similarly, the finding that grasses and flowering plants were beginning to colonise part of Antarctica - another powerful image - was the first story that began to bring reporting of global warming out of the doldrums, at least in Britain.

We are also much better at reporting *conflict* than the process of reaching *consensus*. In Britain, many of our institutions are confrontational - Parliament, the law courts, trades unions and management. The media understands issues that fall into this confrontational matrix and tends to see those that do not - like the environment - as irrelevant and unimportant. Indeed we often report the process of seeking scientific consensus in a confrontational way. Thus having put forward one conclusion based on a particular set of findings, we often seek a contrary view and give it equal weight, just as we would in reporting Parliament or the law courts. This is one reason why the media made such a mess of reporting the debate over global warming, giving equal space and weight to a handful of dissident scientists as to the overwhelming consensus of the vast majority, expressed in the conclusions of the Intergovernmental Panel on Climate Change. In part, this stems from a sound journalistic instinct, always to be seeking to challenge established wisdom: but it also stems from a failure to understand how science operates. Even groups that exploit the media's concentration on confrontation, like Greenpeace, get frustrated by it: they complain that they cannot get the same publicity for their work on solutions, like their promotion of their ozone-friendly Greenfreeze fridge, as they do for their protests over the Brent Spar or nuclear testing in the Pacific.

All this is made even more difficult by the conservatism of the media, which does not easily take up new issues. The environment is a new subject that was not around when many editors and other executives formed their news values. Worse, it has come in waves - reaching peaks of newsworthiness at the beginning of the 1970s and between the late 1980s and early 1990s and declining sharply afterwards - which has made it seem dated as well as unfamiliar.

Then, in Britain at least, the national media often tends to reflect the concerns and views of a limited number of people, concentrated in the small area that encompasses Westminster, Whitehall and the City - the centres of politics, administration and business. The issues that preoccupy this group often seem to leave the rest of Britain cold while some of the concerns that animate the country as a whole often fail to penetrate this inner circle. However, as commercial organisations, fighting tight circulation battles, newspapers will eventually find that they cannot continue to underplay such a popular subject as the environment. Surveys continually reinforce this message. Those carried out on the *Observer* during my time on the paper showed that the environment came top when readers were asked which subject in the paper most interested them, and second when they were asked what they wanted to be given more space. Other newspapers have had similar findings.

Environmental issues will also increasingly force their way into the news agenda because environmental processes will increasingly express themselves as events. This will in turn provide an appetite for knowing more about the processes behind the events. The spate of floods across the world in recent years have forced themselves onto the news pages, but have also led to increasing discussion of such contributing factors as deforestation, the canalisation of rivers and climate change. I have never known a time when there were so many environmental stories around - and largely ones being thrown up by natural, economic and political processes rather than being manufactured by NGOs or politicians for their own purposes.

The media will therefore, I believe, despite all its limitations, slowly play an increasing role in the environmental debate.

The Role of Education

David Bellamy and Alastair McIntosh

In the year 387 BC, 482 years before the writing of the Apocalypse, Plato established the first university. It was called 'The Academy', from which we get the word academic, and it was visited by Socrates. Most of what we know about Socrates is from Plato's writings. Socrates saw that philosophy is essentially about life. In his comment 'we are discussing no small matter, but how we ought to live' (Republic VIII 352d) he showed that he shared a common concern with mankind today.

Today the highest award given by our universities is a doctorate in philosophy - a teaching qualification in *philosophia*, literally the love of the goddess of wisdom. When we speak of academic excellence today, we are drawing on the tradition of the Greek word *orete*, meaning all round virtue or excellence. We can see from Plato's Timaeus and Critias how Greek debate was conducted within the framework of a profound understanding of ecological history. The Critias refers to the detrimental effects of felling the thick woods of prehistoric Greece. The rich soft soil had all run away leaving the land wasted and the springs and streams dried up. Plato goes on to describe how the great oaken beams in disused temples are the only record of the springs of the gods who were once worshipped in those places. This bears out what science has now proved about the effects of deforestation.

Socrates' own relationship with nature is a telling one, reflecting the ambivalent attitude towards learning from nature apparent in so many academics today, yet Socrates had the humility and the wisdom in the end to admit the narrowness of this view. Plato portrays this beautifully in the Phaedrus. Phaedrus meets Socrates wandering barefoot in Athens, persuades him to leave the town and the pair wander out to a grove by a river. Once there, Socrates is overwhelmed by such a delightful resting place. Chastening himself for having been unaware of what nature had to offer to the thinker, Socrates begs forgiveness for having presumed that nature could not teach anything to a lover of learning. Filled with inspiration, he then goes on to show that the endeavour to know love is the central motivation and goal of the philosopher. Without love there is no wisdom, only dry learning. Socrates concludes his dialogue with Phaedrus by thanking the spirits of nature for having inspired him with lofty thoughts. It is perhaps in this context that we should weigh up Plato's decision to locate The Academy, the first university, not amongst the spires and towers of the town but outside the city, in a wooded grove.

What of modern universities and education? In our experience nearly every university around the world today is becoming a groveless academy. Car parks grow where trees once stood. Playing fields are sold off to supermarket lots. Life is filtered and packaged into virtual reality. We are in danger of producing graduates more comfortable with the computer than in relating to a living community, either of people or of nature. If it continues down this track, the modern Academy, the university, will become a betrayal of philosophy because young minds are being deprived of the insights of the ancients within the very institutions that were founded on their wisdom.

Just how far the prostitution of our universities is going is exemplified in Britain by the Government's 1993 white paper on Science, Technology and Engineering, entitled 'Realising our Potential'. It calls for fundamental cultural change in order to accord academia with the needs of government and industry. It stresses wealth creation as the acid test of relevance and seeks interaction on a much larger scale 'between scientists and businessmen involved in the day-to-day business of selling in competitive markets'. A whole chapter is devoted to the military industry. Worst of all, we are told that our children are to be inducted into all this through the radical agenda of changes in the school curriculum and throughout the whole education and training system that this Government has embarked upon.

We are not critical of everything in the white paper. There is actually much in it to praise the government for. It addresses the role of the scientific community for the first time in 20 years and it calls for better integration between pure and applied science. It remarks that the history of the United Kingdom has shown the intimate connection between free trade, the application of science to tradable products and national prosperity. It rightly attributes the creation of the modern world to the British Industrial Revolution and warns that in a world where ever fiercer competition prevails, history's lessons are highly pertinent. However those lessons have not been learned. In India and elsewhere thousands of the world's poorest farmers and fishermen have been remonstrating with their governments not to sign GATT, the global agreement on trades and tariffs. In London the Department of Trade and Industry has been advising British businessmen selfishly to exploit the low wages of countries like Vietnam.

When Ananda Coomaraswamy was born in Colombo in 1877, the people of Sri Lanka still grew many of the 280 plus varieties of rice which had been developed and sustained by their considerable population for more than 2,500 years. The average family was self-sufficient from an area of no more than two hectares. Their culturally diverse lifestyles focused on a complex system of irrigation fed from stable catchments covered with tropical rainforest, which provided them which much of utilitarian value. Their population growth was contained by social practices and, in all probability, the use of a fungal-based oral contraceptive. Today all this has changed. Only some 27 of those rice varieties survive, 'safe' in high-tech gene banks, and only four are widely planted. The diverse forests have gone, replaced by monoculture, the irrigation tanks are full of silt, and malnutrition, mass unemployment and social unrest stalk one of the most beautiful corners of the earth. Similar stories from all over the globe fill our newspapers. In his book *Sources of Wisdom,* Poon the Swami warned that the contentment of innumerable peoples can be destroyed in a generation by the withering touch of our civilisation.

Against this background, what is the role of education and of the church? First and foremost, perhaps the most important task for education is to recreate the ritual of the family by celebrating the fact that bringing up children and the maintenance of the extended family is the most spiritually challenging and the most worthwhile occupation in the world. Secondly, education should aim to recreate the ritual of village life within the urban sprawl which will soon be the habitat of over 60 per cent of the human population. What people need is a nuclear centre based on the church, the school, the shop, the pub or the coffee shop: an extension of the family, a place where everyone, including children, knows they are safe. Thirdly, education should put the fourth R into the school curriculum, the R in environment, however it is defined. This is the resource through which all other subjects should be taught and all decisions made. We should be learning to praise God through a scientific understanding of the bounty of created evolution, to appreciate being part of God's environment and God being part of our environment. The Bible, the Talmud and especially the Koran all teach us that the most important ability of creation is to praise God. Humankind alone has the ability to learn from these books, to read them and act on the light they shed on the world.

Society and governments must be made to realise the following things. Firstly, they must be made to realise the importance of small farms and small farming and fishing communities as the architects of sustainable land care and coastal zone management. They do not have to be reinvented, they have existed and been sustainable for centuries and they should be allowed to continue that sustainability. The conservators of the world's gene banks must understand the importance of grazing animals in the management equation and that both Cain and Abel were omnivores, not vegetarians. We cannot run the world on the basis of vegetarianism: animals are far too important. Secondly, they must realise that, as the water of one third of the world's river basins are expected to provide for the needs of two or more countries, crops and cropping systems which use less water are therefore an urgent research priority. Thirdly, they must develop crop varieties and systems which use less pesticides and fertilisers. These products make farming too expensive and competitive. While they have resulted in a massive increase in grain production (by 1986 the science of the so-called Green Revolution had helped the world provide enough grain to feed six billion people - a fantastic achievement), they have not solved the problem of malnutrition. In that same year, India produced 24 million tonnes of surplus grain and yet still was home to half the world's malnourished people. They were simply too poor to afford the price of the food. The development of crop varieties and systems which use less pesticides and fertilisers would also benefit our own farmers in the EU, who are constantly told that they are working in an increasingly competitive world. If we can scale down the inputs and maintain the output we will be winning. Reduction of the use of pesticides and fertilisers, hand in hand with the proper use of human waste, would also have positive spin-offs with regard to the now critical world-wide problem of galloping eutrophication - the enrichment of our lakes, rivers and seas.

We also need to refurbish the world's river systems so they can naturally deal with flood control and tertiary sewage treatment. Thank goodness this is now beginning to happen. Across the world civil engineers are putting river systems back into working order. The people of Germany have demanded that the upper Rhine is given back its river rain forest. The people of Belgium, Holland and Germany are putting the river Meuse back into working order, taking out the straight, concrete channels and putting back the meanders. In China they are feeding 1.2 billion people by recycling human sewage and running whole agri-industrial complexes on greenhouse friendly fuel - biogas. Shanghai still produces over 70 % of her food within the city, based on recycling human sewage. That's sustainability.

Why, when world governments spend multimillions on fisheries research, don't they take any notice of their scientists when it comes to repeated warnings of gross over-exploitation of 9 of the 17 so-called fish boxes? Why aren't more academic and scientific voices raised against the continued destruction of the world's natural vegetation? The world is in desperate need of an arbitration council, which can rapidly come to decisions regarding the validity of research and action on environmental matters without the dubious ethics of a white paper which stresses wealth creation as the acid test of relevance.

At his capital trial, when charged with teaching subversive views to the youth of Athens, Socrates said in his defence, 'if, in your annoyance, you will finish me off with a single slap, then you will go on sleeping until the end of your days, unless God, in his care for you, sends someone to take my place.' World conservation needs the ethics of the Academy more than ever before. We must not allow philosophy to be failed. The cause of world conservation needs to become more than just a source of business, in research grants and consultancies, to our universities. Instead, it should be their most important *raison d'etre*, for the earth itself hangs in the balance.

God in his wisdom set humankind apart from all the other products of creative evolution by the power of conscious thought. When asked what was his greatest disappointment in life, Mahatma Gandhi answered, 'the hard-heartedness of the educated'. Nevertheless, I am still an optimist. Why? Because I have a grandson, because I have faith in God and because I have faith in science. I believe that the revelation of the Apocalypse is that the sustainable regeneration of the piece of real estate which we in our arrogance have called planet earth is indeed possible.

The Role of the Individual

Alexander Fostiropoulos

In our task of courageously confronting and tackling the very serious problems now threatening our environment, we can gain much insight from bringing to the discussion the hugely important but often misunderstood and misused text of the Book of the Revelation. Nevertheless, real change will only take place when each and every one of us has also begun to make a difference in some area of our personal lives. All of us has the possibility to make a personal response. We may cease to do something which we did before that was wrong. We may notice that we have begun to do something that is good, which we never did before, and not because someone told us to or because circumstances are forcing us to change, but because it springs from within our heart, from within our very being. In every situation, the response that makes a difference is a personal one.

Since the beginning of time man has been confronted with problems and difficulties. He has been frightened by these problems but he has also had many signs and warnings about them. The prophets of ancient times have been no less significant in their warnings than the prophets of our own times. Yet we can so easily find our hearts becoming hardened because we somehow convince ourselves that whatever we do will make no difference at the end of the day. What appears to matter is only what can be done beyond us at government level, at church level, by others in the society at large. However, until things begin to matter to us personally, nothing will change. This life that you and I are now living is a precious and sacred one. Each and every one of us is a custodian of the sacred gift of life which is literally slipping through our fingers. Each of us must ask, 'What is going on in my personal life? What role can I play?'

A few weeks ago I was travelling to visit a small community in southern England. I visit this group once a month, and often think over what I am going to say to them in the sermon as I drive to see them. It is about an hour and a half's drive on a Sunday morning. On this particular occasion I remember having to stop at the side of the road and take stock when the words of the Gospel text for that day hit me. The words that struck me in that particular passage were those that Christ addresses to anyone who approaches Him and asks to follow Him: 'He who wishes to follow me, let him deny himself, take up his cross, and follow me' (Matthew 16: 24).

I suddenly realised that both as a minister in His church, but even more importantly as a person, I am following Christ, only in as much as I have denied myself and taken up my cross. It is only in doing this that I may call myself a believer in Christ. This is a personal experience, but I realised that despite appearances, something is already happening in my life, the denial of myself, and the carrying of my cross, which changes everything. This is what makes change possible. Everything fell into place, as it were. This personal response is the only way I can make a difference. Without it I am powerless. Moreover, as I was going to visit that relatively small community, I recognised that this was what brought us all together. I saw the importance of realising that this is not just an individualistic matter, something that has happened in my own life, in isolation, but there is a similar process going on in everyone around us.

Whatever our particular contribution in the great matters that challenge us today, such as the environment, it is going to be but a part of a process that is going on in perpetuity. However urgent a problem seems, we cannot be in the business of quick fixes. It may well be that each and every one of us has to live with the frustration that we may never see the results of our plan of action. Furthermore, the manner we do things matters. All our efforts need be sustained at a personal level and pursued in a way that will never embarrass or embitter our neighbour.

It is a tragedy that sometimes we isolate ourselves with our fellow professionals, with fellow human beings who are equally powerless, and in the process convince ourselves that we are addressing the problems effectively, when at a personal level, in our own lives, so little is taking place that makes a difference. It is even more tragic that we are becoming set in this rigid pattern and therefore not exercising our creative freedom. Although it is true that whenever we meet and talk about important matters, our understanding of things will be refined and maybe deepened through a sharing of our ideas and through a common plan of action, the real question is whether there is a sustainable change at a personal level.

Time is passing by, the time we have left in which to make a difference. Yet time is also the dimension within which our own moments of revelation are received. The Greek word *kairos* expresses a glorious notion - the right time, the appropriate time for things to happen. Revelation comes in such a way that it makes personal action inevitable at the moment of disclosure. This notion is at the heart of the Christian tradition in the definition of the moment of the start of the celebration of the Eucharist, the time when all things are ready for the Lord to act. In our own lives there are such significant moments, and they define our course of action.

I hope that when we share such moments in debate and discussion, we will be able to learn from them and take them with us for further use. They will not only enlighten our minds and perhaps increase our knowledge, but will also act as moments of awakening or revelation. I find the analogy of an alarm that wakes us up from our sleep very helpful in this regard. Throughout our lives we are being woken by a series of alarm bells that are ringing at significant moments. They are ringing because it is the right time. Yet so often we fall back into sleep, just as we did when we were young children and our parents woke us up. You may remember what those moments were like. We did not want to be woken, we wanted to go back again into that comforting and reassuring experience of sleep!

No system, no problem, no situation, no place presents an insurmountable problem for the human spirit created as it is in the image of God. Let us adopt as our motto the declaration of man before the presence of God, in the words of the Psalmist, 'I shall not die but live, and declare the works of the Lord' (Psalm 118: 17).

Chapter 7

The role of religious institutions

Introduction

Richard J C Chartres

The institutional embodiment of religious traditions has often excited impatience and suspicion even among those who have counted themselves devoted explorers of the intellectual and mystical aspects of religion. It must be confessed that there is sometimes a degree of corruption of an original inspiration in the process of institutionalisation. The competition for power among religious institutions has in the past evidently damaged their spiritual authority and has been a potent ingredient in some of the most sanguinary conflicts of history. This has contributed to the pervasive feeling noticed by Professor Thurman in his concluding piece in this section that 'religion is part of the problem'.

Truth must, however, be embodied in the life of a community before it can realise its full creative potential and this embodiment inevitably necessitates the construction of institutions. The conviction which unites many of the contributors to this section is that religious institutions have a crucial though as yet undeveloped role not only in alerting world opinion to the environmental dangers which confront us but also in mobilising energies in the search for a sustainable life together in which 'nation shall not lift up sword against nation, neither shall they learn war any more but they shall sit every man under his vine and under his fig tree and none shall make them afraid' (Micah 4:3-4).

Religious bodies are free from some of the pressures which inhibit political parties as they seek to make a contribution to the debate on the environment. Religion deals in ultimates and religious institutions do not have to be dominated by the short term-ism which is induced by the prospect of the next election. It is also true that in many places in the world, religious bodies and leaders enjoy a level of trust which is the envy of politicians and reach to parts other educational agencies cannot reach.

The challenge lies in assembling a new generation of religious leaders world-wide who are both really representative and have a global vision of the threats to the common good which we face and the possibilities of common action. There is also a need to develop more adequate religious institutions to respond to the opportunities opened up by the revolution in global communications without replicating the bureaucratic structures which properly belong to other kinds of international bodies.

In a world of great complexity, however, the temptation is to retreat into the certainties of the ghetto of piety and to pursue antique polemics in the face of our common environmental danger. Religious leaders need to listen to the voice of the scientific community and vice versa. One of the most remarkable aspects of the Revelation and the Environment symposium was that this 'listening' did happen.

Scientists and theologians alike paid close attention to the presentations from the various religious traditions brought together in this section. From the very first words of Mehmet Aydin's helpful paper the theme of a common ethical approach to the use of nature is obvious. There is work continuing on an international basis in an effort to devise some statement of a global ethic and the papers detail some of the common ground upon which such a declaration could be built.

As well as echoes from one tradition to another there are also direct connections, noticed for example in Paul Mendes-Flohr's homage to St John of Patmos from the Jewish perspective. 'Apocalyptic' was of course a genre of Jewish literature but Professor Mendes-Flohr does not omit to acknowledge the influence of Zoroastrian ideas and gives us a paradigm of interfaith dialogue in the work of the Patmos Circle in the 1920's. There may be a model for contemporary Patmos symposiasts in the journal of the Patmos Circle *Die Kreatur* which was jointly edited by a Jew, a Protestant and a Catholic and which addressed the most exigent social and philosophical issues of the day from the perspective of faith but without a confessional emphasis.

Some religious traditions insist on a commitment to a particular way or revelation and certainly little spiritual progress is made by simply browsing in a supermarket of religious options. The commitment and highly disciplined life described by Rajwant Singh has its parallels in all religions but a non-exclusive confidence in one's own religious tradition need not obscure the wisdom to be found in other ways. On the contrary a marked antipathy to other spiritual paths and teachers is nearly always associated with an immature state of spiritual development in which there is an all too evident admixture of ego-projection in the picture of the God one claims to be worshipping.

The papers in this section are a contribution to the genuine dialogue based on knowledge and respect which must accompany any discussion of how the world's religions can best respond in bringing Revelation to bear fruitfully on the Environment.

Qur'anic Revelation and the Environment

Mehmet S Aydin

It is interesting to note that although the great religions of the world exhibit theologies quite different from each other, their approach to nature is very much alike, especially where the question of how nature is to be used is concerned. It must be remembered that this question, when it is taken within a religious context, is primarily an ethical one.

This commonality is extremely important and it ought to be worked out as systematically as possible. In this time of ours when the ecological perspective has become very important in relation to economic and political perspectives in general, the different religions could achieve much if they could work on common projects in the light of a new global theology of the environment. To achieve this task, the holy scriptures have provided us with rich materials and enlightened directions. For example, when one reads the Qur'an attentively, especially the chapters revealed in the Meccan period, one cannot fail to see that 'talk of nature' becomes an essential ingredient of 'talk of God'. In other words, nature is at the centre of the Qur'anic discourse. This is understandable, since amongst the many 'ways to God' the place nature occupies is paramount. This is the reason why it constitutes the real starting point in all theistic arguments for the existence of God, developed within different religious traditions under the name of 'natural theology' - another common element in all theistic religions. The philosophical guise of this theology may make us forget that it was originally religious consciousness which paved the way for such speculations. The rise and growth of that consciousness without which there can be no religion, owes a great deal to nature.

As we all know, Muslims believe that the Qur'an is the 'Word of God', and together with the adherents of many of the great faiths of the world, they also believe that the world is the 'Work of God'. As a matter of fact, when this 'work' is read religiously, it too becomes the 'Word of God' in a different sense, since both revelation and nature lead humankind to the Ultimate Reality. The Qur'anic revelation thus uses the term 'sign' both in referring to its own verses as well as natural phenomena. They are each 'signs of God' (*ayat Allah*). This terminology is not accidental. It rests on the belief that 'the same God who created nature and displayed His wisdom therein so clearly has also revealed the verses (*ayat*) of the Qur'an'.[1] In other words, both are the *logoi* of God.

It is due to this God-nature relationship, that nature possesses its createdness and contingency, as well as its rationality, orderliness, and purposefulness. It is due to the same relationship that the ecological discourse within the Islamic perspective cannot dispense with the thoroughly theistic background enunciated by the Qur'an. Human nature too exhibits analogous characteristics and this is evidently one of the reasons why the Islamic tradition terms nature itself 'muslim' in a symbolic or even cosmological sense. In an oft-quoted verse the Qur'an says:

> He (God) said to them (the skies) and to the earth: 'Come both of you, willingly or unwillingly!' (To which they responded) 'We do come in obedience.'[2]

It should be pointed out that 'to come to God willingly and in obedience' is one of the primary definitions of the Qur'anic term 'Islam', and it only secondarily refers to the ramified religious tradition.

This primitive meaning of 'Islam' seems to have stirred an extremely strong mystical emotion, especially in the hearts of the Sufis who were attached to what is usually called 'the Yasawi School' with which practically all Turkish Sufi orders have organic ties. These Sufis accept all creatures of God as 'brothers in faith', or to be more precise as 'brothers in love'. That is why our beloved Yunus Emre, the Turkish Sufi poet of the thirteenth century says:

> With the mountains and the rocks
> I call you forth, my God.
> With the birds as day breaks
> I call you forth, my God.
> With Jesus in the sky,
> With Moses on Mount Sinai,
> Raising my sceptre high -
> I call you forth, my God.[3]

This whole philosophy - so to speak - of participation and interrelation finds its ultimate roots in the Qur'an which says that 'There is not a single thing but extols His limitless glory and praise, but you fail to grasp the manner of their glorifying Him.'[4] Another verse asks 'Do you not see that to God bow down in worship all things that are in the heavens and the earth - the sun, the moon, the stars, the hills, the trees, the animals?' [5]

Underlying all such images is the idea of a systematic teleology in the cosmos. Specifically, such Qur'anic terms as *husban* (suggesting 'mathematical computation'), *mizan* ('the balance of justice') and *qadar* or *taqdir* ('God-given role' or 'function') indicate, among many other things, the purposefulness of the creation. Of this, God says:

> We have not created the heavens and the earth and all that stands between

> them in sport, but We created them only for a serious end (*bi'l-haqq*), though most of them do not understand.[6]

This purposefulness reaches the level of self-consciousness in the life of man, who himself is an integral part of nature. One of the 'serious ends' for which nature is created is the existence of humankind as an ethical creature, that is, a being capable of self-criticism and ethical self-realisation. Nature seen in the light of the Qur'anic revelation, is thus ultimately a theatre for the moral activity of humans, 'for the purpose of confuting evil and error with truth and value'.[7] Humankind is equipped with all the means to achieve this end. Nature for its part is created in readiness to receive the good results of the efficacious activity of humans, and to make their input successful. The man fulfilling such a function is termed by the Qur'an *muslih*, that is a 'good (*salih*) reformer' of nature and society.

The figure posited by the Qur'an as the opposite of the *muslih* is the *mufsid*, that is, the individual in the habit of corrupting both nature and society. According to the Qur'an:

> Corruption has appeared on earth and sea, as an outcome of what men's hands have wrought, and so He may give them a taste of some of their deeds in order that they may return (from evil and corruption).[8]

With such corruption of the earth, man betrays the trust (*amana*) given to him by God, and abandons his vicegerency of this world (*khilafa*, an important Qur'anic concept). By doing so, he closes himself to the God-given bounty which is expressed in the Revelation by the term *taskhir*, that is, the subservience of nature to humans for the purpose of moral and aesthetic perfection, and never to be exploited for corruption.[9] Any one familiar with the contents of the Qur'anic revelation knows well how the theme of 'corruption on the earth' (*fasad fi'l-`ard*) occurs there again and again. Muhammad Asad, the well-known Austrian convert to Islam, rightly interprets the above verse as a now verifiable prophecy:

> The growing corruption and destruction of our natural environment, so awesomely - if as yet only partially - demonstrated in our time, is here predicted as "an outcome of what men's hands have wrought", i.e., that self-destructive - because utterly materialistic - inventiveness and frenzied activity which now threatens mankind with previously unimaginable ecological disasters.[10]

There is no doubt that the 'corrupting hands' are only the external instruments of people who are themselves inwardly, that is morally, corrupted. Corruption thus starts within man's inner life, then extends to the social and eventually the natural order. 'There is a kind of man', says the Qur'an, 'who whenever he prevails, goes about the earth spreading corruption and destroying agricultural land and offspring. But God loves not corruption.'[11]

The Qur'an accepts all animal species as 'fellow nations', when it says, 'No creature is there crawling on the earth, no bird flying with its wings, but they are nations like yourself.' [12] This attitude towards animals has had a lasting effect on the institution of Muslim pious foundations (*waqf*, plural *awqaf*) which still play a very significant role in Muslim communal life. In many documents of *waqf*, there are special articles related to the preservation of animal life. In many buildings owned by *waqf* foundations in Istanbul and elsewhere, we see 'bird castles' (in Turkish, *kus saraylari*) and special places to feed stray cats and dogs. The well-known French thinker Montaigne talks in his Essays about special Turkish hospitals for animals.[13]

According to the Islamic tradition, caring for animals brings reward both here and in the world to come. In one of the traditions attributed to the Prophet Muhammad we read the following:

> Someone said, 'O Messenger of God, will we then have a reward for the good done to our animals?' 'There will definitely be a reward' he replied, 'for anyone who gives water to a being that has a tender heart'.[14]

The same thing is said about the person who plants a tree: 'Never does a Muslim plant trees or cultivate land,' says the Prophet Muhammad, 'and birds or men or beasts eat from them, but that is charity on his behalf'.[15]

In order to have an overview of the Qur'anic perspective on the environment, one should also pay attention to the frequent descriptions of Paradise (*janna*) in the Revelation. These are obviously important for anyone interested in Islamic aesthetics, but their environmental dimension should not be underestimated. The Qur'anic Paradise is 'the eternal home' and 'home of peace'[16] (*dar as-salam*) for the righteous who will dwell 'in the midst of gardens and rivers'[17] - rivers whose water is 'incorruptible' (*ghair-asin*).[18] In it, there are companions who are 'pure and holy' (*mutahhara*).[19] And again in it there is 'no vain discourse' (*laghw*), that is, no corrupt and corrupting words.[20]

We all know that here we are not living in Paradise, but at least traditionally we maintained a sense of analogy which enabled us to entertain a proper conception of Paradise while moulding our earthly environment. How about the generations to come? What will become of them if they are to inherit a morally polluted interior landscape within a seriously polluted natural one?

1 Fazlur Rahman, *Major Themes of the Qur'an*, p.72

2 *Qur'an* 41:11

[3] Yunus Emre, *Selected Poems*, Trs.T Halman, Ankara, 1990, p.158

[4] *Qur'an* 17:44

[5] *Qur'an* 22:18

[6] *Qur'an* 44:38

[7] Eg. *Qur'an* 21:18

[8] *Qur'an* 31:41

[9] See I.R. al-Faruqi and L L al-Faruqi, *The Cultural Atlas of Islam*, New York 1986,

p.314 ff.

[10] M.Asad, *The Message of the Qur'an*, Gibraltar, 1980, p.623. Significantly the primary meaning of *fasad* is not ethical but biological degeneration, that is, putrefaction.

[11] *Qur'an* 2:205

[12] *Qur'an* 6:38

[13] For further information see M Bayraktar, *Islam ve Ekoloji*, Ankara 1992, p109

[14] *Sahih al-Bukhari*

[15] *Sahih Muslim*

[16] E.g. *Qur'an* 39:73-5

[17] E.g. *Qur'an* 54:54

[18] *Qur'an* 47:15

[19] *Qur'an* 2:25

[20] *Qur'an* 19:62

Zoroastrianism and the Environment

Shahin Bekhradnia

'Four thousand years before the first Greens, the priest-prophet Zoroaster preached that humankind, as the seventh creation, must protect the other six and keep the earth fertile and unsullied.' So noted the *Independent* newspaper published in London on 15 May 1990.

The dates surrounding Zoroaster's (or Zarathustra's) life are contested but contemporary academic thinking, based on linguistic analysis of the oldest part of the religious texts (the *Gathas* which were embedded in the very centre of the major religious scriptures) suggests that he received his revelation from Ahura Mazda in the middle of the second millennium BC. It is suggested that he came from Azarbaijan although more credence is now being given to a birthplace in Eastern Tajikistan.

Although Nietsche, Strauss and others (principally in the nineteenth century) used Zoroaster's name in their writings, reflecting a fascination with recently discovered Oriental philosophers, they revealed little understanding of the principles taught by the Iranian prophet.

Many people, while having vaguely heard of Zoroastrianism, associate it with fire-worship. In fact respect towards fire is akin to respect for the cross amongst Christians. By contemplating fire, Zoroastrians are reminded of the creative energy force which they call Ahura Mazda or Wise Lord, whose creation is so bounteous and perfect. The fire which radiates light also represents that perfection or purity of being and consciousness which Zoroastrians are exhorted to strive towards.

Some people may have encountered Zoroastrianism through Parsees. Parsees are those Zoroastrians who in the ninth century fled from Iran by boat to India in order to find a more tolerant ambience in which they could practise their religion without the harassment to which they were regularly subjected in Iran after the Arab/Islamic conquest. In India the Parsees (thus called as they came from Persia) flourished and were highly favoured by the British who groomed them to achieve exceptional social, political and economic successes.

The population of the community is minute in relation to other world religions. Around the world there are probably no more than a mere 150,000 Zoroastrians, of whom about 75,000 live in India, about 30,000 in Iran, and the rest have dispersed around the globe (particularly since the Islamic Revolution in 1979). The Parsee population has fallen rapidly from a peak of 125,000 a century ago, while the Iranian Zoroastrian population has grown from a mere 7,000 survivors at the end of the nineteenth century to 40,0000 at the end of the twentieth century.

Often described as the first of the great world religions, Zoroastrianism is a monotheistic religion although those who have only a superficial understanding of it get bogged down by the idea of dualism. Some have called Zoroastrianism a system of ethical dualism. Certainly the importance of its teachings on the subject of right and wrong is known to many churchmen of the Orthodox tradition.

Closely associated with this ethical dualism and the stress upon conscious choice to choose the righteous path (or *asha*), is the concept of independent free will and choice. According to the religion, we are all born with a conscience and we make a choice to follow either good or evil, each of which will bring its own consequences at death. In Zoroastrian tradition our souls cross the bridge of judgement on the fourth day and those whose evil deeds outweigh their good deeds are condemned to an afterlife in an eternally unpleasant abode, while those with a credit of good deeds will pass to an abode of everlasting happiness. These eschatological ideas are of course also to be found in the Judaeo-Christian tradition, but few realise that they owe their origin to Zoroastrian concepts.

Although the pursuit of *asha* offers comforting prospects of the afterlife, the main tenets of the religion stress the here and now, for Zoroastrianism is a pragmatic teaching concerned with an improvement in the quality of life on earth. Thus to pursue *asha* brings its own immediate rewards in the form of friends, love, food, security, health and harmony. The psychological benefit from an easy conscience at peace with itself is something to be desired and which can be achieved by all who strive towards it.

To understand what *asha* is, Zoroastrians are taught to contemplate or meditate upon nature, to observe its beauty, the order and regularity of the natural cycles, and the harmony and interdependence of its manifestations. Through such meditation one will arrive at an awareness of God's presence and in a peaceful and balanced state of mind one's thinking will be clear and the choices to be made will be apparent. Meditation does not necessarily have to be achieved through a state of inactivity; indeed Zoroastrians are exhorted to work hard and exert themselves physically on the land since a healthy body will aid balanced thinking.

We are taught that *asha* is practised by maintaining moral purity of thought and word as well as through some of the deeds discussed above - hence the Zoroastrian motto: 'good thoughts, good words and good deeds'. This translates into telling the truth and being honest in all dealings and transactions with others. While this may appear to be an essential aspiration of all religions, it is interesting that non-Zoroastrian writers, from Herodotus to French and British travellers in Iran and India from the early seventeenth to the late nineteenth centuries, make specific mention of the high degree of probity and integrity they encountered among Zoroastrians.

Asha, which means purity, may be pursued at many different levels. On a physical level, we may strive to be pure or clean in the surroundings of the house and home, in our clothing, and in our body. The air we breathe, the water we drink and the land we cultivate have to be kept pure and clean in the pursuit of *asha*. It is taught that if we act as responsible stewards of the natural elements, we will reap the rewards of plentiful food, absence of illness and pleasant surroundings. The neglect of the environment will amount to turning our back on the pursuit of *asha*, resulting in a capitulation to the forces of darkness and evil in contrast to light and goodness/virtue.

In practical terms, Zoroastrians plant a tree to celebrate the birth of a new family member and do not place the dead in the ground - this would be seen as polluting the nourishing earth. Zoroastrians regard it as a sin to wash in running water, but instead draw the water off to perform ablutions and clothes washing. Their ability to harness water to irrigate the earth goes back to ancient times when the famous underground water channels, *qanats,* were constructed to avoid evaporation and contamination and to bring fresh water to settlements. The wedding liturgy specifically reminds newly weds that they carry a duty to maintain the purity of running water and to bring under cultivation any abandoned land, while if there is marsh land nearby they should drain it and make it salubrious.

Because of their understanding of the relationship of human kind with earth and water, Zoroastrians became renowned gardeners and farmers, the famous gardens of Darius at Pasargardae being the best example of such skills in antiquity. In more recent times both the Safavid and Qajar kings in the sixteenth and nineteenth centuries respectively created new capitals first in Isfahan and then in Tehran. To provide gardens fit for a king, both dynasties employed Zoroastrian gardeners to create them.

The result of successful husbandry, which includes the care and protection of animals, is a surplus of food produce. As another dimension of *asha,* Zoroastrians are expected to share the benefit of their success and prosperity within the community. Hence great importance is attached to charitable acts which may take the form of communal feasts, foundation and endowments of schools, orphanages and hospitals and other beneficial deeds.

The significance of the natural world pervades all aspects of Zoroastrian culture, so that all rituals and practices reflect this. For example each of the twelve months of the year carries the name of one of God's creations such as the earth, the water, the sun, the wind, the animals, and the plants and each of the thirty days within each month also carry the names of one aspect of God's creation. When the name of the month and the name of the day coincide, it is considered a holy day and feasting and prayers take place. On four days each month there are meat fasting days, *nabor* (lit: no cutting), which are particularly associated with animals.

Nowruz, the Iranian national New Year on the first day of spring is celebrated by all people of Zoroastrian origin, in Kurdistan, Afghanistan, Tajikistan and in Iran. Significantly it is the only Zoroastrian festival to survive Islamisation and the traditional ceremonial table of *haft s(h)in* on which seven of God's nourishing creations are displayed is still faithfully maintained in every household throughout the Persian speaking world.

The festival of water, *Tirgan*, is a joyous celebration of water in the height of summer, while the fire festival, *Sadeh*, in the middle of winter, is a thanksgiving for the discovery of fire and for the approaching new year at spring. The festival of *Mehr* or *Mithra* in autumn consists of communal eating and praise, while the six annual festivals known as *gahambar* are five day-long occasions when feasts are held in memory of deceased people who have endowed land and its produce to benefit the community. The whole community is expected to partake of such feasts.

At these *gahambar*, at weddings, initiations and at the death anniversary memorial (*sal*), a fire urn burns fragrances such as sandalwood, incense and myrrh. A cloth is set out, decked with evergreens, a collection of dried fruits and nuts, fresh green sprouting grain or lentils and opened fruits. Often the cloth will be green, the cover of the book of prayers, the *Avesta*, will be green. Green is the colour favoured alongside red for the traditional female costumes and certainly for bridal costumes; emeralds as a dowry have been popular for some time. Green, the symbol of abundance, is thus represented through many dimensions of cultural practice.

The importance of abundance and fertility is reflected in a section within the *Avesta* (Vendidad 3:32 & 3:4): 'agriculture is one of the noblest of all employments because he who sows grain, sows righteousness', and 'one of the most joyous spots on earth is the place where one of the faithful sows grain and grass and fruit bearing trees, or where he waters ground that is too dry and dries ground that is too wet' (quoted in Williams Jackson 1906: 373-4).

The practice and teachings of Zoroaster place the respect for and stewardship of the environment in a central position. It has thus been culturally absorbed and is deeply embedded in all aspects of life. The ritual practices, the prayers and the festivals which members of the Zoroastrian community share, all reflect and give thanks for the creation of the natural elements on which life depends. The ideology is passed down through parental practice and is reinforced by community values and formal education. It is indeed as much a religion that is practised as it is one that is professed.

Paradigms of Revelation: the Embrace of East and West

William S Hatcher

> Effort must be exerted ... that East and West, like unto two longing souls, may embrace each other in the utmost love ... (Abdu'l-Bahá)

There are at least two fundamental ways of seeing the relationship between a whole and its parts. One way sees the whole as the sum of its parts (an explicit axiom of Euclid) and thus seeks to understand systems (wholes) by understanding each component (part) of the system. This is the tradition of Western thought, beginning with Greek atomism and ending with modern physics, which sees each physical system as a more-or-less complex configuration of elementary particles. In this view of reality, the worth or value of a system is almost directly proportional to its complexity.

Complex systems frequently have a *modular* structure, in which larger components of the system are themselves systems formed from smaller components. Modularity of structure allows for extreme specialisation and individuation of the components of a system. A typical (and in some ways prototypical) example of a modular system is the human body, which is a complex configuration of maybe a trillion cells. The modular organisation of the body is reflected in the fact that the body's cells are not uniform, but highly specialised, where similarly specialised cells are grouped to form tissues, similar tissues form organs, similar organs form systems and the body itself is formed from the interaction of its systems.

There are both advantages and disadvantages to modular organisation. The advantages are solidity, stability and the emergence, in extremely complex systems, of higher-order properties of the system, that is, properties of the whole that do not exist in the parts. For example, the human body has the property of autonomous location, but an individual cell or organ does not have this property. The disadvantages, especially in relation to modular social systems, are rigidity, stratification (for example, social and economic classes), pyramidal, top-down authoritarianism, and a tendency to overspecialisation or over individualisation of the components with resulting fragmentation, competition and conflict.

The understanding of a whole by an exhaustive analysis of its parts has, beginning with Descartes, led to modern science. But it has also led to mechanism and materialism. The reasoning is simple: since God is clearly not present in the parts (that is, the elementary particles) then He cannot be present in the whole since the whole is just the sum of its parts. Thus, either God does not exist at all or else He exists only metaphorically as a higher-order property of complex systems.

One can, of course believe, as Descartes did, that there is a spiritual realm of existence parallel to the realm of physical systems. But from the Cartesian viewpoint, this 'other world' has no real explanatory value or relevance to the operation or administration of material systems. In other words, if it makes us feel better, we may choose to believe that such a realm of spirit exists, but when it comes to the administration of physical or social systems, the spiritual realm is seen as essentially irrelevant. This is the famous Cartesian duality, which holds that the observable world can be explained in itself without reference to spiritual reality.

There is, however, another way of seeing the relationship between whole and part, one which gives rise to the notion of a *distributed system*, a system in which the whole is reflected or reproduced within each part. In such a system, there is no individuality of the components; rather, each component is a representative of the whole.

The (proto)typical example of a distributed system is the human brain: any given brain cell can assume any brain function and is thus a reflection of the brain as a whole. Indeed, it is now known that such mental functions as perception, memory and feeling are not localised in any specific part of the brain but are instantiated in a series of *clichés* by electroform waves that sweep the entire brain at regular intervals of extremely short duration. This operational distribution gives optimal flexibility to brain functioning, but exists only because the brain is part of the modularly organised system of the entire body (in which, for example, the vital needs of brain cells are provided by the body's circulatory system). At the same time, the functioning of the modularly organised body is harmonised and unified only because it is directed by the distributively organised brain. Thus, both modular and distributed systems are needed, and the optimal functioning of each type of system depends on the other.

In adopting Greek philosophy as its basic language, the Christian religion adopted also the modular view of social and political structures, thereby giving rise to the various hierarchical structures of church and state that have characterised the social expression of Christian civilisation down through the ages. Indeed, the Judaeo-Christian-Islamic religions have all tended to generate these types of structures.

Nowhere has the view of reality as a strictly modular system found greater expression than in the Christian paradigm of revelation as incarnation, which asserts that God Himself (the pinnacle of the hierarchy) has become *wholly* incarnate in a localised part of reality (that is, the physical person of Jesus of Nazareth). Thus the incarnational model of revelation is the ultimate expression of the world view that sees reality in a modular way.

However, the Hindu-Buddhist religious tradition has always been based on the view of reality as a distributed system, in which each part represents the whole. Buddha's statement of the Golden Rule is typical of this: 'Be kind to your brother, for he *is* yourself.' It also finds value in the simple and not just the complex. But, just as the dualistic Christian view eventually gave rise to the conception of revelation as incarnation, so the Hindu-Buddhist view that 'all is one' gave rise, in at least one of its major expressions, to the pantheistic notion that 'everything is God'.

Gradually, each of these notions of revelation gave rise to distinct metaphysical doctrines and, finally, to competing religious ideologies. On the one hand, the dualism of the Judaic religions tends to see physical reality and its laws as lower and thus less valuable than spiritual reality. This can, under certain circumstances, lead to an attitude of disregard for the essential sacredness of the created world. On the other hand, Hindu-Buddhist monism tends to blur the distinction between higher and lower, good and evil, part and whole. While this view respects the sacredness of nature, it does not always generate a value paradigm that empowers humans, as the highest element of creation, to relate effectively to nature. In time, subgroups have appeared within each camp, leading ultimately to the present social configuration in which the religions of the world appear as so many competing ideologies or belief systems.

The fact that both modular and distributed systems are reconciled in the reality of the human being suggests that the incarnational and pantheistic paradigms of revelation, and their various doctrinal refinements, could also be reconciled. Such a reconciliation is in fact part of the explicit teachings of Bahá'u'lláh, Founder of the Bahá'i Faith. Bahá'u'lláh teaches that the creation, though not a literal part of God, is nonetheless sacred in that every created thing reflects some of the attributes of its Creator. However, the human being is the highest creation of God, because only humans are capable of reflecting, in some measure, *all* of the attributes of God.

Here is one passage in which Bahá'u'lláh expresses this truth:

> Upon the inmost reality of each and every created thing (God) hath shed the light of one of His names, and made it a recipient of the glory of one of His attributes. Upon the reality of man, however, He hath focused the radiance of all his names and attributes, and made it the mirror of His own Self. Alone of all created things man hath been singled out for so great a favour, so enduring a bounty. [1]

Because of this unique, divine endowment, the human being should be a focal point of unity for the whole of created reality. Religion, as the highest expression of the spiritual potential of the human being, should be the greatest unifying force in the world. Nevertheless, prevalent disunity is a major feature of our modern world. Speaking of this disunity and conflict Bahá'u'lláh has said:

> The evidences of discord and malice are apparent everywhere, though all were made for harmony and union. The Great Being saith: O well-beloved ones! The tabernacle of unity hath been raised; regard ye not one another as strangers. Ye are the fruits of one tree, and the leaves of one branch.[2]

Is it not paradoxical that religion, which should be the greatest source of unity and co-operation in the world, is so often perceived as a source of conflict and disunity? Indeed, materialists often seem more united against the spiritual view of reality than are the spiritually-minded united among themselves.

Some would undoubtedly say that inter-religious conflict is the inevitable consequences of doctrinal differences between religions. However, religious believers have a fundamental choice in their dialogue with each other and with the world: they can choose to emphasise their differences or to emphasise what they have in common. Perhaps the greatest response religion could make to the various challenges of the modern world would be for religious believers of all doctrinal schools to unite in affirming what is universal and unifying in religion rather than what is particular and divisive. No genuine, particular metaphysical insight, of whatever doctrinal school of thought, would be undermined or diminished if the present discourse of differentiation were replaced by a discourse of integration and unity among the religions. For example, we all believe that creation is sacred because it has come forth from a sacred Reality. What a great power it would be in the world if Religion spoke with one voice - and across doctrinal boundaries - on the major issues facing humankind today, including the great environmental crisis we face!

Perhaps then the embrace of East and West as anticipated by Abdu'l-Bahá involves two moves. It means that those of use who inherit the Western tradition of analysis, duality, sharp boundaries and rigid distinctions must learn from the East how to *see* the underlying wholeness of reality. We must replace duality and hierarchical distinctions with a more balanced complementarity such as between male and female, yin and yang. We must correct our tendency to make unnecessary and gratuitous distinctions or individuations, and we must rediscover that power of renunciation taught not only by the Buddha but also by Jesus Christ.

And Easterners can learn through science how to understand and manage a modular system, but without losing their precious sense and perception of those essential connections that are always more important than the attendant distinctions. Indeed, we must all learn how to maintain necessary distinctions without creating unnecessary conflict, as we have too often done in the past.

A change of discourse from division to unity among religions is not yet evident, in spite of the ever-pressing need for such a change. It does seem probable, however, that a significant modification of inter-religious discourse will eventually occur, because the great religious communities of the world run the risk of a substantial loss of moral credibility if they continue to emphasise a discourse of fragmentation rather than of co-operation and unity. As Bahá'u'lláh has said:

> The Purpose of the one true God, exalted be His glory, in revealing Himself unto men is to lay bare those gems that lie hidden within the mind of their true and inmost selves. That the diverse communions of the earth, and the manifold systems of religious belief, should never be allowed to foster the feelings of animosity among men, is, in this Day, of the essence of the Faith of God and His Religion.[3]

1 *Gleanings from the Writings of Bahá'u'lláh,* Bahá'í Publishing Trust p.65

2 *Gleanings from the Writings of Bahá'u'lláh,* Bahá'í Publishing Trust p.218

3 *Gleanings from the Writings of Bahá'u'lláh,* Bahá'í Publishing Trust p.287

Apocalyptic and Prophetic Eschatology - a Jewish Homage to St John of Patmos

Paul Mendes-Flohr

As is well known, Jews prefer stories to theology. Accordingly I shall begin with a tale. It is related that a famed scholar of comparative religion at an equally famed British university once approached a local rabbi with an urgent request for a reference to a judicious introduction to 'systematic Jewish theology.' Baffled, the rabbi quickly regained his Talmudic composure and, with an impish smile, replied: 'Jews don't have a theology, and were we to have one it surely would not be systematic.' Hence, true to ancient Jewish inclinations, I offer some very unsystematic, and thus I hope undogmatic reflections on the Apocalypse as a genre of religious literature, which grew out of the soil of biblical Judaism. To highlight what I discern to be the salient contours of the spiritual landscape forged by this literature, I shall compare it with what may be called the prophetic sensibility. I trust my remarks will also prove relevant to the crystallisation of an ecological ethos.

As an Israeli Jew I feel particularly honoured by this opportunity to pay homage to St John the Theologian, for John of blessed memory was, like myself, also an Israeli Jew. Born and raised in the Holy Land, John clearly received a sound Jewish education as is evident from the many references to the Hebrew Scriptures in the Apocalypse. His hermeneutic and homiletic methods are typical of Judaism. What, of course, is most significant for us is his thorough familiarity with the genre of Jewish literature we now call apocalyptic. This literature arose in about the third century before the Common Era, and was manifestly influenced by Israel's sojourn or exile in Babylonia. Parenthetically, in Babylon our Zoroastrian sisters and brothers made a seminal contribution to the ideational structure of the apocalyptic imagination.

Apocalyptic literature - which was vast and undoubtedly filled several library shelves - marked a decisive and far-reaching development in Jewish messianism or eschatology. No longer did the Jews regard their redemption merely in national terms; redemption would now include all of humanity, all the world, and, indeed, the cosmos itself. The longed for messiah will bring in his wake not only the restoration of Israel's national glory, but also eternal peace among all peoples and the renewal of creation. Apocalyptic literature sets the horizons of the Jewish eschatological vision until this very day.

Yet here we encounter a grand paradox. The apocalyptic literature was for the most part resolutely rejected by the custodians of normative Judaism, the rabbis. What we know of this literature is due largely to the various Christian churches. Some of the apocalyptic books - for instance, Baruch and the Second Book of Esdras - were included in several Christian versions of the Old Testament canon, and others were incorporated in the Apocrypha and especially the collection of writings called the Pseudepigrapha. Still other books occasionally surfaced in the course of the centuries, from long forgotten sources. Among the most significant were the cache of manuscripts discovered some fifty years ago in the caves above the Dead Sea.

Other than the Book of Daniel (and passages in other biblical books, such as Ezekiel 2:8, that have an apocalyptic character) the rabbis recognised and honoured none of the apocalyptic books. Why? There are several reasons for the rabbis' opposition to this literature. The overarching reason, I believe, is theological. The rabbis - who, incidentally, cast as Pharisees are unjustly maligned in Western thought as spiritually barren legalists - were troubled by the tendency of apocalyptic literature to bifurcate or polarise humanity between the damned, the incorrigibly evil ones, and those who are graced, deemed good and therefore destined for salvation. This polarisation of humanity offended the democratic sensibilities of the rabbis who held that each individual, no matter how corrupt, can repent, or as we say in Hebrew 'return' and reclaim moral freedom and responsibility.

This conception of religious merit was associated with the biblical prophets. Indeed, the rabbis adhered to a prophetic conception of eschatology. The prophets revealed a vision of the future not merely as a grammatical or temporal category, but as an alternative reality. The future, the prophets insisted, need not be a repetition of yesterday and its maladies, nor need it be a replication of today and its troubles. The future, as envisioned by the prophets, may be fundamentally, indeed ontologically different from all that went before. However, the future disclosed by the prophets is but a divine promise; its realisation depends on us. We are, so to speak, partners with God in paving the way to the future, a time redeemed from sin and woe. Here the idea of justice comes to the fore, a notion richly elaborated by the rabbis.

The prophetic responsibility placed on humanity, the rabbis taught, requires more than compassion or even love, it requires justice. Justice is a political notion; it thus entails jurisprudence, or if you like legal procedures, and hard, onerous work in an ever complex world. In this sense, justice is a pre-eschatological or pre-messianic concept; it is what we - individually and collectively - do in the here and now in an imperfect, unredeemed world. But lest our actions in the here and now get lost in pragmatics, we are beholden to keep the vision of the messianic future and promise in mind. Here is where Jewish ritual and liturgy play their role. As a spiritual exercise, the rites and prayers of Judaism also serve to remind one that justice without compassion and mercy can go astray. As the Jewish medieval mystics would have put it, justice and compassion are like a bride and groom; without their coupling divine love remains forlorn and fallow.

Despite Judaism's theological commitment to prophetic eschatology, it did not entirely abandon its apocalyptic heritage. Even the Talmud, the principal corpus of rabbinic teachings, makes furtive but telling references to apocalyptic ideas, especially the *eschaton* (the end of days) as marking a renewal of creation. The sense of urgency that informs the apocalypse recurrently gripped Jews throughout the ages. In practically every generation there were Jews who were overtaken by premonitions of an imminent catastrophe, and the concomitant need for a radical, revolutionary renewal of the fabric of society and ultimately the very foundations of the created order. From this perspective, much of Jewish spirituality may be viewed as an unresolved tension between prophetic and apocalyptic eschatology. One particularly significant attempt at a resolution was promoted by the kabbalists, Jewish mystics. In sixteenth century Palestine, kabbalists hailing from Spain and North Africa (some coming via Greece and Greek Anatolia) developed the notion of *tikkun olam* - literally, 'repairing or healing the world'. These kabbalists held that the political and social woes afflicting Israel and humanity were ontologically linked to some basic cosmic disharmony. Expressed in more parochial terms, Israel's anguished exile was but a reflection of the exile suffered by Creation itself. To redeem the world from its agony and, correspondingly, Israel from its exile, the sacredness of all aspects of the created order must be redeemed. God certainly does His or Her part in *tikkun olam*, and we humans are beckoned to share in this process which takes place both in the natural and the social order. Through prayer, meditation, ritual and good deeds (which include sound political activity), we help redeem the world, restoring it to its pristine divinity. The way we greet a rainbow or the setting sun, the way we interact with our fellow human beings - all affect the destiny of the world and creation. The kabbalists' doctrine of *tikkun olam* is akin to what Metropolitan John of Pergamon has called in his elegant lecture 'the liturgical ethos'. What distinguishes the kabbalists is the sense of urgency and intensity with which they pursued the task of redeeming creation. If we are lax, if we should neglect our responsibility, they held, the agony of humanity and creation will, in fact, deepen - and thus also our sin and guilt. This teaching of *tikkun olam* continues to shape Jewish religious and spiritual sensibility.

In the twentieth century, there is yet another Jewish response to the apocalyptic impulse that directly connects with both the Apocalypse of John and the theme of our symposium. During the First World War, the Jewish religious thinker Franz Rosenzweig and his friend Eugen Rosenstock, a Christian of Jewish provenance, founded what they called the Patmos Circle. Borne by a conviction that not only Europe but all of civilisation was on the edge of a profound catastrophe, they drew inspiration from John the Theologian. John's teachings that the Logos, the Word, must be renewed spiritually and practically through the renewal of actual speech, that is, the conduct of everyday life, was their guiding light. Utter catastrophe awaits us, they taught, unless we recognise that we are all creatures of God, that each of us is a child of God, who through the gift of life has been given the awesome but unavoidable responsibility to care for each other and for divine creation. In this task we should, nay must, draw inspiration from John's vision of the coming Age of the Spirit, which the Patmos Circle understood as an age in which creation would gain full glory and a truly human society would unfold. It will be a time in which all human beings will live fully in the Spirit and the Word. It is the age longed for by both Jew and Christian, but it will also be a time when one will feel inadequate simply to be a Jew or a Christian.

From 1926-29 the Patmos Circle had a journal, appropriately called *Die Kreatur*, the Creature. The journal had three editors - a Jew, Martin Buber, a Christian, Viktor von Weizsäcker, and a Catholic, Josef Wittig. They pointedly solicited contributions from the likes of the great Orthodox Christian Nikolai Berdayev, and the Hindu Rabindranath Tagore. The articles of *Die Kreatur* were neither confessional nor theological, however. From the perspective of faith, the journal addressed the most exigent social and philosophical issues of the day, including what we would today call those of ecological interest.

The spirit of the journal and the Patmos Circle is perhaps best captured by an article penned by Franz Rosenzweig. Entitling his essay, 'Ökumene', the Jewish philosopher explored therein how a truly human world or ecumenical order, bound by the Logos and our consciousness of our common creatureliness, could come to pass. Rosenzweig appended to his essay an allegory, to which he gave as its title the Greek term *thalatta*, the sea. This was the inebriated cry of Xenophon's troops who, after years of wandering, reached the Aegean waters leading homeward to Hellas. From time immemorial, Rosenzweig explains, the sea has either intimidated humanity because of its 'yawning chaos' or has summoned us to embrace it. The eschatological thrust towards the *ökumene* is determined by the latter movement, for the seas of the world ultimately flow one into another, endowing the world with continuity and unity. That unity is our home: *thalatta* - the sea, homeward.

A philological-cum-theological postscript

The sages of the Talmud rendered the Greek term *telos* (end, the goal or objective of a process) as *takhlit*. In Yiddish, the folk-tongue of the Jews of Eastern Europe, the term underwent an interesting phonological and conceptual transformation. In Yiddish *takhlit* became *tachlis* - a term that has penetrated various European languages, English, Dutch, German, and Russian. *Tachlis* denotes concrete, practical deeds; thus the phrase 'let's get down to *tachlis*,' brass tacks. Hence, *takhlit* - teleological, indeed eschatological talk - requires *tachlis*, down to earth actions in the here and now. This is true both for an eschatological and an ecological ethic.

A Hindu Perspective

K L Seshagiri Rao

> Let there be peace in the heavens, the earth, the atmosphere, in the water, the herbs, the vegetation, among the divine beings and in Brahman, the absolute reality. Let everything be at peace and in peace. Only then will we find peace.
>
> (Shukla Yajurveda 36:17)

The Hindu ethical ideal, comprehensively described as *dharma*, gathers in its sweep the total well-being of humans; it includes physical, moral, intellectual, and spiritual values. *Dharma* is both individual and social, this worldly as well as other worldly. It is both stable and flexible. It provides for continuity, it can be related to new times and conditions. It contains a code of life and a philosophy of social and ethical relations.

Hindu ethics is inspired by the ideal of *Loka Samgraha*, 'protection and welfare of the world' taught in the Bhagavad Gita (III, 20), the most popular Hindu scripture. This ideal reveals a deep concern with human happiness and the stability of society. It requires from each member of society a way of life consistent with the general welfare of mankind.

In the third chapter of the Gita, Sri Krishna elucidates this ideal of the 'welfare of the world'. He says that action or dynamism is a characteristic of life. For humans, there is no escape from action. The only question is: what kind of action is worthy and valuable? Sri Krishna's answer is that any action that contributes to the welfare of the whole world with all the living beings in it, is valuable; and that which harms or hinders it is a negative value, and therefore immoral or *adharma*. The positive forces of life promote, and the negative forces of life hinder the conditions of general welfare and fulfilment of mankind. A sacrificial act (*Yajna*) is an altruistic and at the same time a most creative action. The conception of *Yajna* was much widened in the Bhagavad Gita, distinguishing the spirit of *Yajna* from its forms, and endowing it with a content that is at once social and ecological. Those acts which protect and enhance public utility and fulfilment are called *Yajna*.

Sacrificial performance has a cosmic concern; it is intended to reinvigorate the powers that sustain the world by securing cosmic stability and social order. It activates the positive forces of the universe, it brings rain and secures protection from degeneration.

Anything done for the benefit of society and the world is a sacrifice, and conversely every sacrifice is conducive to material prosperity and spiritual growth. The spiritual motivation for the act undermines egocentric materialism, orients our aspirations and initiates us into altruistic work, from which the whole world benefits.

Nature is a source of raw materials. These natural resources are given not for selfish exploitation by one group or nation or generation but to be shared by all creation. The natural elements of air, water, fire, sky and earth are all life-giving and life-promoting. They heal and rehabilitate, turning toxic materials into wholesome things.

Water sustains and preserves life on earth. It is one of the commonest of all substances, constituting about two thirds of the earth's surface. Of this, 0.01 % consists in pure ground water from all the lakes, streams, rivers and rainfall, which is unevenly distributed throughout the world. Today water has become scarce due to the profound damage to the global water system. But without water, there can be no agriculture, fruits or vegetables. Actually, water is not only an environment for life, it is part of life itself.

Flourishing civilisations developed historically on river banks. It is at these centres that trade, commerce and transportation developed and connected the world with ideals of religion, philosophy and science. Rivers are considered holy; for this reason they and their confluences became places of pilgrimage in ancient cultures. Ceremonies of initiation and death were, and still are performed at these places. It is because of their life giving and life fulfilling properties that the appellation 'mother' is bestowed on them, as with the Ganges, which becomes *Ganga Maiya.*

Hindus regard the earth also as mother, deserving our reverence. She feeds us, provides us with shelter and with material for our clothes; without her gifts, survival is impossible. If, as children, we do not take care of her, we diminish her ability to take care of us. Unfortunately, our industrial achievements are undermining the natural environment to such an extent that the earth itself has now become an area of concern.

Human short-sightedness and selfishness have propelled us into ecological crises of immense proportions. Natural resources are being depleted and degraded rapidly on a global scale. Industries are polluting the atmosphere, releasing chemical wastage in water. They are using up non-renewable energy resources without a thought for posterity. Exhaust fumes from millions of automobiles are causing acid rain. Chemical fertilisers, pesticides and herbicides pollute the air, water and vegetation, harming human health and welfare and even causing genetic damage. The disappearing ozone layer threatens our children with cancer, blindness and death. Global environmental problems cast into doubt our continued existence on the planet.

Hinduism speaks of harmony with nature and with the whole creation. It speaks of the moral and spiritual laws of life as precious parts of the very structure of the universe. These laws are expressed in terms of truthfulness, humility, unity of humanity, reverence for life and care of the environment. Hindus have chosen their places of pilgrimage on tops of mountains, or the banks of rivers, wherever there was some natural beauty or grandeur. They speak of father sky, mother earth and uncle moon. Rivers such as the Ganges, Jamuna, Godavari, Cauvẹri and mountains such as the Himalayas, Vindhya and Malaya are considered sacred, because they are life giving, life sustaining and life promoting. The same is the case for oceans and trees.

Religious leaders can and must impress upon their followers the importance of the cleanliness of river waters and the protection of forests and mountains. In this connection, the childhood and early life of Sri Krisna - the eighth incarnation of God - spent among the cowherds is very inspiring. He is concerned with the preservation of the life sustaining waters of Jamuna, the life promoting Govardhan mountain, and the life supporting qualities of the animal world in Vrindavan. The Supreme Divinity plays with common, simple and pure cowherds (*gopas* and *gopis*). Bred in this atmosphere, Sri Krisna endears himself not only to his contemporaries and humanity at large, but also to all creatures and the natural environment.

It is important to make mention not just of physical pollution but also of mental pollution: for this is the underlying cause of physical and environmental ravages. Greed, lust and anger are the causes; disharmony, conflict, sickness and degradation of nature are their results. They are the result of the desire for profit, power, and self-aggrandisement. For the important thing about actions is the psychological and social motivations that drive them. All actions start in the mind, which in turn is the expression of the ego: if the ego is allowed to grow, it generates anger, greed, lust, hatred, and it makes life miserable for all. All of these vices should be sacrificed in the fire of self-purification. The mental - and not just the physical - environment has to be kept clean and focused. *Yajna* is the sacrificing of one's ego and the burning of impurities. When it is accomplished, it is not just oneself but also one's society and environment that are purified. A wiser thought, a cleaner vision and a greater kindness appear then honesty, love and selfless service emerge in life.

Whenever worship-service is performed in the Hindu tradition, it is preceded by purification of the elements, *bhutasuddhi*. The five elements are purified both within and without. Purification is the pre-requisite for sanctification; it establishes harmony between the macrocosm and the microcosm. The offerings that are made to the deity represent the best of each of the five elements: the fragrance offered represents the essence of earth, the offering of a flower represents the sky (openness, blossoming), incense represents the wind, water represents itself, and light represents fire. Only when these elements are pure or purified, can they be offered in worship.

All forms of life are an integral part of nature. All species need to be appreciated and respected. There are birds, fishes, and animals of all kinds. As life on this planet is a single weave, the value of the non-human world is to be recognised. It is not there for exploitation. Human and non-human creations are interdependent, not isolated. We are participants in a vast affirmation of life in *all* ventures. Such an outlook could on the one hand, reverse the trend to degrade the environment, and on the other help to enrich it. In this endeavour, traditional prescriptions, transmitted orally, are still in order:

> Cause wells to be dug; cause trees to be planted; cause water tanks to be built; cause flower gardens and parks to be made; wherever you cremate a dead body, plant a tree; don't cut green trees; don't pluck flowers at night; don't disturb water at night; let foreign particles settle down; don't pollute river banks; make life-styles less violent and less extravagant; minimise consumption and minimise the harm to the environment; reuse and recycle durable materials; enhance the quality of life, not just the standard of living; encourage interfaith dialogue and support for environmental protection.

Nature is our friend, not our enemy. We are born and live and play in the lap of nature and receive sustenance from her; our debt to nature is therefore immense, and it is incumbent upon us to discharge our debt by giving back a fraction of what we have taken from her. Nature is not to be exploited or conquered, but to be nourished and cherished. We should develop friendly and responsible relationships with nature.

To conclude, it may be worthwhile to contemplate briefly the life of a tree: it gives its leaves to animals; shares its flowers with bees; gives its fruits to peoples; provides shelter to birds and insects; takes carbon dioxide and gives oxygen to the living world. Finally, it sacrifices itself to be used as construction material or as fuel. It lives and dies for the service of others. However, it never asks anything in return: the least humankind can do is to offer it our appreciation and goodwill.

According to the Atharvaveda, a Vadic seer stood in front of a mighty tree thousands of years ago and addressed it thus:

> May the axe be far from you;
> May the fire be far from you;
> May there be rains for you without storms;
> May you be blessed Mighty tree,
> And may I be blessed too.

Sikhism and the Environment

Rajwant Singh

Creating the world, God has made it a place to practice spirituality.[1]

The Sikh scripture declares that the purpose of human beings is to achieve a blissful state and to be in harmony with all creation. It seems, however, that the human race has drifted away from this ideal.

The demands of national economic growth and individual needs are depleting natural resources, and there is serious concern that the earth may no longer be a sustainable bio-system. There is a sense of crisis in all parts of the world.

This crisis reintroduces the basic question of the purpose of our presence as human beings in this world. We are called to the vision of Guru Nanak which is of a world society comprising God-conscious human beings, to whom the earth and the universe are sacred. Guru Nanak laid the foundations of Sikhism in the late fifteenth century. His writings, and those of the other Sikh gurus who succeeded him, as well as those of other spiritual leaders, are included in the scripture, the *Guru Granth Sahib*. The *Guru Granth* has been the effective guru of the Sikhs since 1708, when Guru Gobind Singh declared that there would be no more human gurus. The name *sikh* means disciple or learner of the Truth.

Guru Nanak would diagnose the increasing barrenness of the earth's terrain as a reflection of the increasing emptiness within humans, and he would say the first step in solving the problems in our world is spiritual, and lies in prayer and accepting God's *hukam*. It is difficult to translate certain Sikh concepts accurately. *Hukam* is one such concept - it may be best described as a synthesis of God's will or command, and so 'system'. With an attitude of humility, and surrender to the Divine Spirit as manifest in the *hukam*, conscientious human beings can seek to redress the current crises of the environment and social justice. In the Sikh way this is done through the guidance of the guru, who is thought of as the Divine Master in his role of messenger of God.

A Sikh theologian, Kapur Singh, explains that Sikhism has three postulates implicit in its teachings. Firstly, there is no ultimate duality between spirit and matter. Secondly, human beings have the capacity to participate consciously in the process of spiritual progress. Thirdly, the highest goal of spiritual progress is harmony with God while remaining earth-conscious, so that the world itself may be transformed into a spiritual plane of existence.

Unity of spirit and matter

An important Sikh doctrine is that, as the product of God's activity, all parts of the universe are holy. God is an all-pervasive being manifest in the various elements of creation. Every form in this world is a manifestation of its Creator.

> The Creator created Himself....
> And created all creation in which He is manifest!
> You Yourself the bumble-bee, flower, fruit and the tree.
> You Yourself the water, desert, ocean and the pond.
> You Yourself the big fish, tortoise and the Cause of causes.
> Your form cannot be known.[2]

The Sikh view is that spirit and matter are not antagonistic. Guru Nanak in fact declares that spirit is the sole reality and matter only a form of spirit:

> When I saw truly, I knew that all was primeval.
> Nanak, the subtle (spirit) and the gross (material) are, in fact, identical.[3]

This is the ultimate basis of the Sikh belief that harmony with God directly entails that human beings endeavour to live in harmony with God's creation. As we will now see, this first postulate strongly informs the second and third.

Spiritual progress through discipline

The second postulate is that people are capable of further spiritual progress by maintaining a highly disciplined inner life. It is not required that human beings outwardly renounce the world. They must maintain their life in it and uphold their worldly responsibilities. Sikhism simply teaches against a life of conspicuous, wasteful consumption. The gurus in fact recommend the judicious utilisation of the material resources available to humans, and teach them to respect the dignity of all life, whether human or not. Such a respect for life can only be fostered when one first recognises the Divine spark within oneself, then sees it and cherishes it in others. As the *Guru Granth Sahib* says:

> This little shrine of the human body!
> This great opportunity of life!
> The object is to meet the Beloved, thy Master!

The concrete method suggested by Guru Nanak by which we may fulfil our vocation of spiritual progress, involves meditation, prayer, and mastery over five negative forces: lust, anger, materialistic attachment, conceit and greed. These together constitute what Sikhs term '*haumai*' - literally 'I am-ness'. Mastering *haumai* is achieved by developing five positive forces: compassion, humility, contemplation, contentment, and selfless service (*seva*). As the home itself is an ideal environment for the exercise of these disciplines, the Sikh religion preaches strong family involvement and a person pursuing private spiritual discipline must also work to create an atmosphere for other members of the family to progress spiritually.

Transformation of the world

The third postulate is that the true end of human beings is their emergence into God-consciousness, while remaining aware of the world. The product of this dual focus is an intense desire to transform the world into a higher plane of existence. Through a life based on the method prescribed by the gurus, individuals may achieve this transformation. Such truly emancipated, valiant and enlightened spirits (*jivan-mukta, brahma-gyani*) become the real benefactors of humanity and the world around them. In this God-conscious state they are yet involved in human problems and society commensurately with their realisation, proving their effectiveness there. The emancipated person thus lives with the mission of the emancipation of all! A true Sikh is fervently in favour of human rights, the environment, and justice:

> The God-conscious person is animated with an intense desire to do good in this world.[4]

Practising the philosophy

Environmental concerns must be viewed as part of the broader issue of human development and social justice. Many environmental problems, and in particular the exploitation of resources in developing nations, are due to the poverty of large parts of the population. In view of this an integrated approach becomes necessary.

The tenth guru founded the Order of the *Khalsa* in 1699, for those who practise the spiritual discipline of Sikhism. Over the last three centuries the members of the *Khalsa* have stood up for the rights of the oppressed even at the cost of their own lives, maintaining the *Khalsa* vision of a global society as framed in the *Guru Granth* itself:

> Henceforth such is the Will of God:
> No man shall coerce another;
> No person shall exploit another.
> Each individual has the inalienable birth-right to seek and pursue happiness and self-fulfilment.
> Love and persuasion is the only law of social coherence.[5]

The *Khalsa*'s members have opposed any force that has threatened the freedom and dignity of human beings. In the eighteenth century it was the oppressive rulers of northern India, and invaders from Afghanistan. In the nineteenth and twentieth centuries its members struggled against the oppression of European colonists and Indian governments. The ideal of the *Khalsa* is to strive for justice for all, not merely for its own members.

The institution of *sangat, pangat* and *langar*

The Sikh gurus all actively challenged the caste system in India. Guru Nanak said:

> There are the lowest men among the low-castes.
> Nanak, I shall go with them.
> What have I got to do with the great?
> God's eye of mercy falls on those who take care of the lowly.[6]

So it was that the Sikh gurus in their travels preferred the homes of those who made an honest living, to the homes of those who thrived on exploitation. The Sikh gurus also moulded new traditions to engender a more equitable society. In consequence they created institutions that still form the basis of Sikh society. They invited people of all castes and creeds to meditate together - an institution called *sangat* - and either before or after this meditation, the participants were asked to sit and eat together irrespective of their background, termed *pangat*. The Sikh gurus moreover started a tradition of freely distributing food to the poor, called *langar*. These three ideas, still much alive today, were in contrast with Indian society, which had separate temples or wells for social outcasts.

Equality of women

Any solutions to the problem of the environment must be sensitive to women's concerns, and must include women as equals. Piecemeal solutions to environmental problems will merely focus, for example, on limiting population growth through family planning measures which often end up abusing women's rights, and should be rejected on those grounds alone.

Sikhism contains important lessons on this. Guru Nanak and other Sikh gurus advocated equality for women and took steps to implement this. Nanak denounced the idea that spirituality was only for men, and not for women. Guru Amardas in the sixteenth century advocated widow marriages and strongly opposed the custom of *sati* - the Indian practice whereby widows burned themselves with their husband's corpse at cremation. He appointed a large number of women preachers, and at least one bishop - Mathura Devi - four hundred years ago. The Sikh gurus also raised their voice against the *purdah* or veil. Amardas did not even allow the Queen of Haripur to come into the religious assembly wearing a veil. The immediate effect of these reforms was that without the burden of unnecessary and unreasonable customs, Sikh women became the temporal and spiritual colleagues of men, often acting as their conscience, and have proved themselves to be the equals of men in service, sacrifice and bravery. Since the late nineteenth century individual Sikh men and women, in various cities and towns, took the initiative to start women's colleges and schools, and women's education was part of a general drive to improve education among the Sikhs initiated by Sikh organisations in the 1920s.

Community-based sharing of resources

Traditional modes of life in Northern India have involved large numbers of people depending upon relatively limited resources. Keynotes are minimal consumption, recycling and sharing of resources. Traditional practices have maintained lands and forests in the vicinity of human settlements as community property. For instance in rural Punjab an important feature of the Sikh *gurudwara* (temple), is the community land which surrounds it. This is not used for agriculture, but instead has groves providing shelter and a source of firewood. Moreover most *gurudwaras* were specifically designed with artificial lakes, or were located near natural water-sources such as rivers or pools which were always considered a community resource. For instance, Amritsar grew up around the *Harimandir* (known as the *Golden Temple*) and the *Amrit Sarovar* (the *Pool of Nectar* - a reference to the water).

Since the time of the gurus, the Sikh *gurudwara* has included institutionalised practices that emphasise sharing. In addition to the functions already mentioned - as a place to congregate for prayer and meditation, and as a community kitchen - the *gurudwara* also traditionally functions as a place to stay for travellers, a place for dispensing medical care, and a place to educate the young.

Conclusion

Sikhism regards a co-operative society as the only truly religious society, as the Sikh view of society is grounded in the worth of every individual as a microcosm of God. Therefore an individual must never be coerced, or manipulated:

> If thou wouldst seek God, demolish and distort not the heart of any individual.[7]

Sikhs believe that an awareness of that sacred relationship between human beings and the environment is necessary for the health of our planet and for our survival. A new 'environmental ethic' dedicated to the wise use of the resources provided by a bountiful nature, must start with a dedicated application of our tried and true spiritual heritage.

1 *Guru Granth Sahib* p.1035

2 *Guru Granth Sahib* p.1016

[3] *Guru Granth Sahib* p. 281

[4] *Guru Granth Sahib* p.273

[5] *Guru Granth Sahib* p.74

[6] *Guru Granth Sahib* p.15

[7] *Guru Granth Sahib* p.1384

Jainism

Laxmi Mall Singhvi

The Jain perspective has to be understood in the context of the larger Indic perspective: the Vedic, the Buddhist and also latter-day developments such as Sikhism. This is because, in certain respects, all these perspectives have much in common, while also representing distinct traditions. In addition to having been the cradle of these various indigenous traditions, India has hospitably received other traditions from outside. In the very first century AD, there was the arrival of Christians who were typically hospitably received and have exercised their freedom of religion throughout two millennia. Similarly, Jews and Zoroastrians were received into India, providing a significant trans-cultural bridge. Islam too found a receptive host in India. So have other sects and denominations. The Bahai faith is a recent example. That is because the true Indic tradition uniquely provided for affirmative acceptance without loss of distinctive identity and without hostile confrontation.

Jainism is itself a particularly ancient indigenous perspective amongst all the faith traditions found in India. The last of the twenty-four exponents of Jainism (known as Tīrthankaras) lived in the sixth and seventh century BC, while the twenty-third lived in the ninth century BC. Between the successive tīrthankaras, there was generally a space of a few centuries. If we worked our way backwards in this way, we would be going back a very long time. Of the two ancient Indian traditions, namely, the Vedic, and the non-Vedic tradition of the *Śrāmanas* (which is represented by Jainism and Buddhism), the Jains are monastic. It was an austere tradition. Its guiding principle could be summarised in the aphorism 'non-violence, *ahimsā,* is the supreme religion'. Modern Indians have taken their inspiration from different aspects of the various religious perspectives encountered in the Indian sub-continent, and it is a matter of profound pride for the Jains that Mahatma Gandhi found in their religious teachings his own principle of non-violence - the principle message, in fact, of his momentous life and work.

It is important to remember that Jainism does not subscribe to the doctrine of a created universe, and instead believes in a beginningless universe without a creator. Moreover, it believes that the universe will never end, and so subscribes to a doctrine of continuous cosmogenesis. It is, however, fair to say that in spite of this distinctive difference which constitutes a significant point of departure, the Jain concept of the soul, its transmigration and the doctrine of *karma* (the generation of a soul's future destiny through its past actions) all correlate with the other perspectives of ancient India.

Jainism believes in an ethics centred not so much on rights but much more on ethics centred on obligations. This is a fundamental principle in the Indic traditions in general, and Jainism for its part, tried to establish that in the ultimate analysis, it is the individual's fulfilment of his or her own responsibility that is indispensable for the maintenance of the Virtue (*dharma*) in society. 'Society' is defined very broadly in Jainism, for flowing from its principle of non-violence is the tenet of reverence for *all* life, not simply human life but extending to animal life at different levels and in theory even to the vegetable kingdom. Jainism thus insists that there must be no destruction, and in so far as this is inevitable in practice, there must at least be no destruction which has not first been responsibly considered. In this context there are two principles which are decisive for Jains. One is the principle of self-restraint (*samyama*). The other is the principle of responsibility represented by the law of *karma*, which lays down that one pays for what one does, or fails to do. Implicit in this is the ethical motivation that springs from Jain belief in transmigration. In that perspective, non-injury will be motivated by the consideration that you yourself, in due course, could be identical with the being that you now harm. This transmigrationist framework thus leads the Jains to a very concrete and pervasive feeling for the universality of life.

The Jain ethic of non-injury *(ahimsā)* extends beyond its obvious physical and metaphysical implications and is intertwined with its epistemology. A little reflection will show that there are many ways of behaving violently, and so it is that we do violence to the truth as such, if we deny its universality and many facets. To insist on a partial aspect of the many-faceted truth is to injure it and to undermine it. One must strive, if one is non-violent, for a holistic approach to truth and this demonstrates the important link between non-violence *(ahimsā)*, pluralism *(anekatā)* and tolerant understanding (*sahishnutā*). These many millennia-old principles of Jainism are relevant to the present-day situation in the world at large.

Jain ideas have a direct relevance to the modern context for many issues of our contemporary environmental crisis for Jainism is rooted in a profoundly ecological world-view. Jainism is quintessentially a religion of ecology, of reverence for life, of sustainable lifestyle. Cosmic interdependence animates Jain ethics. The whole emphasis is on a lifestyle which is in consonance with ecology. As far back as the ninth century BC and indeed for more than a millennia before, there was an emphasis on reciprocity and interdependence, principles that complimented the more 'individualistic' perspective based on private *karma*. Individual and collective aspects of well-being are very intimately related in Jainism. The insistence on vegetarianism, for example, radically equates private purity - and thus individual spiritual well-being - with the well-being of others, human and non-human. This also explains the heavy Jain emphasis on charity, philanthropy and community service, so that all lay-Jains must render community service and offer charity, while the members of the Jain monastic orders must take more austere vows and practise total restraint, self-denial and non-acquisitiveness.

In discussing Jainism in the context of our symposium on revelation and the environment, I am obliged, however, to make a crucial qualification: Jainism does not believe in revelation as such. This non-revelatory position distinguishes it as a 'religion' in addition to its non-theistic perspective. Insight is not acquired or received 'from above' in Jainism but on the basis of the inner illumination and development of the personality. This does not mean Jainism is merely non-theistic and rationalistic. Jainism certainly believes in the efficacy of reason but it is quite prepared to travel beyond the reason of the senses and of pure logic and into the supramental realms of consciousness. The Jains believe that individuals - in principle all individuals - may develop themselves to a point where the boundaries of consciousness are massively extended. Such powerful souls - the Tīrthamkaras, literally 'ford-crossers', the Jain equivalent of prophets - have a clairvoyant faculty, an extra-sensory perception, which gives them the ability to see beyond time and space. There is thus an ultimate expansion of cognition in the conventional sense, but it is called 'perception' and not 'revelation'.

Despite this caveat and proviso, Jainism clearly is deeply relevant to the apocalyptic concern for the environment evoked in this symposium in relation to the Revelation of St John. The Jain religion judges environmental irresponsibility as rigorously as the Biblical revelation. According to the Jain tradition, instead of divine punishment or angry retribution, the crisis ought to be understood in the more impersonal and ethical terms of the inexorability of the law of *karma*, the collective violation of which will inevitably engender a calamitous collective penalty. But the religious conscience of the Jain is overwhelmingly one with that of other believers on this issue; it shares the message of the imperative to live in harmony with the natural worlds and not in incremental conquest of nature. Ecological responsibility is at the heart of Jain faith which gives us a rational and secular framework of reciprocity and interdependence as the basis for a sense of the sacred in the inner and outer space.

I was delighted to hear of the concept of love for animals exemplified in the Christian context by St Francis of Assisi. St Francis of Assisi exemplified the Jain principle of universal compassion and empathy. The Ecumenical Patriarch said that St Francis of Assisi sang the song of a united human family. The revelation of a united human family is the hallmark of the Indic tradition which proclaimed the world as one family and declared that the alienating frontiers which seek to divide humankind trivialise common humanity. In the universal recognition of the revelation of common concern and common cause of cosmic ecology, humanity will find a new sense of purpose and a new sense of fulfilment.

A Jain and a Hindu are able naturally and spontaneously to enter into the experience of different traditions. A Jain or a Hindu thus enters the cave in Patmos in reverence and finds illumination and enlightenment in the awesome apocalyptic revelation which emanated from that cave in the trance of a saint. To understand its message and to relate it to our time and age, we need to go beyond the Biblical words and unravel and decode the imagery and symbolism of 1900 years ago for the comprehension of our generation.

Buddhist Reflections in Honour of St John of Patmos

Robert Thurman

Twenty years ago, when I began to teach at Amherst College in the USA, I taught a freshman seminar called 'Apocalypse or Awakening'. We read the frightening literature on the four horsemen of the apocalypse, on population explosion and megadeath, on pollution and new plagues, on exploitive resource depletion and world famine, and on thermonuclear holocaust and war. It became clear that the overcoming of these grave dangers to all life on earth depended primarily on the mass awakening of a new awareness in a great majority of human beings of all nations.

As we looked through various philosophical, psychological and religious writings it soon became apparent that the question of changing awareness is very much an educational problem. I have been especially excited about this meeting as it seems to me an effort by the leaders of major religious institutions to reach out to co-operate with the leaders of the new world religion called secular humanism, especially the scientists, and address the issue of changing awareness and education. If this can become a long-term working partnership, then scientists will be helped by developing a new respect for the power and importance of spiritual insight into the nature of reality, and religious people will be helped to unify their spiritual practice with broader knowledge of the cosmos and more effective social action.

The Apocalypse of John is both currently and universally relevant for the positive reason that it vividly shows us the New Jerusalem, New Heaven and New Earth, which opens for us a vista of a life when God can no longer be isolated from his creation, when the dualistic split of sacred and profane has been overcome, and where the Christ as Living Love, All-powerful Goodness, and All-knowing Wisdom is interwoven with the lives of all beings. Some might think this itself is a fantasy - but we need this vision vitally, like a daily medicine, in order to keep our hope alive in the midst of all the difficulties. Our greatest enemy now, as in St John s time, the major weapon of the Beast that hammers at us constantly through the media, is hopelessness, despair and cynicism.

We need the medicine of Revelation 21 and 22. We should try to visualise the mandala city and palace, the exalting architecture of the sacred, majestic square city of twelve thousand furlongs width and height, made of jasper, sapphire, translucent gold, with a twelve-fold precious foundation made of the love of the Apostles...we should contemplate this often to learn to feel comfortable with the supposedly impossible, to keep the energy of our inspiration.

The Revelation is also well chosen for another reason. There is a powerful movement of Christian fundamentalism spreading from the US that reads this Revelation as justifying the destruction of the environment. These pious, well-intentioned though rigidly self-righteous people are totally caught up in the imagery of God's destruction of the old world, of Babylon, and have fantasised themselves as those who are earning the New Jerusalem by serving as the horsemen of the apocalypse, assisting in the purificative acts of destruction. They feel justified in a massive defence budget, to make war on whomsoever they choose to demonise. Lindsay's *Late Great Planet Earth* (more than 15 million copies sold) and many other popular books and television mass preachers reinforce this theology of destruction. These Christians consider humanists, scientists, environmentalists, family planning people, women's empowerment activists, welfare advocates - and on and on - as the minions of Satan, the workers of the Beast. Humanist scholars cannot effectively respond to these fundamentalists. They can only be re-educated by leaders of the Christian Churches who must present a clear and persistent critique of the theology of ecocide, and a ringing affirmation that the vision of St John calls for a radical reform of the soul and of society.

I hereby pray for a new Declaration of Patmos in this vein, that it be widely circulated, and that a focused and systematic effort be made to have its main outlines endorsed by leaders of all Christian denominations, including the more moderate evangelicals. I pledge that similar, parallel, and mutually reinforcing efforts will be made within Buddhism in the Buddhist parts of the globe, especially in the last runaway materialist communist nation of China, which is posed to inflict ecocatastrophe on a massive scale, yet where, if the hearts of a new generation of leaders could soften, Buddhist teachers such as HH the Dalai Lama and his many colleagues in other world religions could be of so much help in restoring the spiritual hope of that huge mass of spiritually and emotionally devastated people. The other world religions - with special intensity of appeal to the leaders of Islam - should be invited and stimulated to work in similar ways in the realism of their own religions, and the humanists must exert themselves to critique materialistic nihilism and revive a greed-restraining, life-affirming spiritual humanism. Perhaps a series of Patmos conferences, hosted by the Orthodox, with the leaders of other denominations and religions in dialogue with environmentalists, is in order, from now until the millennium of the common era.

Let me turn now to a Buddhist undertaking of the Apocalypse. In the Holy Teaching of Vimalkirti, a sacred scripture of Mahayana Buddhism that purports to come from Shakyamuni Buddha's time of ca. 500 BCE but by auspicious coincidence emerges as a text in India around the time of Jesus, the theme of Apocalypse and purification is dominant. At the beginning of the Scripture, the Buddha is asked, 'How does the Bodhisattva (a spiritual person who has embarked on the heroic evolutionary path of becoming a perfect Buddha in order to save all beings from suffering) purify and beautify the Buddhaverse?' The Buddhist concept is that a person who becomes perfect in wisdom and compassion transforms and perfects his or her environment which includes other sentient beings at the same time as he or she transforms her own body, mind, and spirit. Thus a Buddhaverse is a universe as perceived by an enlightened being.

The message is remarkably like Revelation in the central respect that the universe as encountered by perfect love is already a perfect place where all may unfold their own highest potential and make their own loving contributions. Love has the power to transform the world, it is the strong force of the atoms of the world - only here it is the collective infinite love of all infinite beings, not conceptually separated as the love of a single, unique creator God. The Scripture states that the Buddhas allow the world to seem full of challenges simply to educate beings, especially in the cultivation of compassion, which requires proximity to suffering to grow. The superiority of such a Buddhaverse to an eternal heaven realm is much discussed, as the 'best of all possible worlds' paradoxes are wrestled with. At the end of the Scripture, Vimalakirti, a Buddha in the embodiment of a lay religious from another Buddhaverse, picks up his home universe, the Abhirati Buddhaverse of Akshobhya, miniaturises it and shows it to the assembly as a sign of hope for them. It is very similar to our naturalistic earth, but the big difference is that the Buddha is visible to all, all of the time, and the giant stairways descending from the lower heavens to the earth are accessible all the time, so the gods can come to earth for a stroll or to hear the teachings, and the humans and other animals can visit the heavens for pleasure, rest and inspiration.

In my reading of the Apocalypse, a key point of Revelation is that the New Heaven and New Earth are not withheld from all beings cruelly or whimsically by God/Christ. How could omnipotence and omni-compassion together produce cruelty? It is impossible. Thus the whole drama of struggle between Christ and the Beast, good and evil, and the tremendous killing, destruction and affliction, must have a pedagogic purpose.

What the krisis and purification drama teaches is that the New World is created by the soul's self-transformation and self-purification. The fundamental sin is that of self-obsession, the self-absolutisation that lies at the root of selfish grasping of pleasure, property, pride and political power through domination of others. The 'mark of the Beast' is the self-addiction of individual self-centeredness, articulated as the delusion of pride of self-abslurisation, the addiction of greed, the explosion of hatred, the poison of envy, and all the attendant vices.

'Blessed are the dead which die in the Lord ...' (14:13) says the voice from heaven before John sees the angels stick their sickles down to reap the earth and pour their seven vials full of plagues that express the wrath of God. Such death and destruction is a cleansing of the ugly crust of sin, breaking the deadly shell of egotism, smashing the prison of self-centeredness, liberating from the slavery of self-addiction. John's vision affirms Jesus' great saying, 'He who saves his life shall lose it, but he who loses his life in Christ, he shall have life everlasting.'

If we wish to save the environment then the bottom line, in this Buddhist reading, is that we must analyse ourselves to find out in what ways we are living in the distortion of self-deification and thereby inevitably depleting, overpopulating, polluting, and destroying the environment, the world. Who destroys the world? We do. How do we save it? We 'die in the Lord', that is kill off our own petty tyrannical ego-habit, give it up and so entrust ourselves to love, give in to our relationality with others, open ourselves through the truth of the ultimate selflessness of our soul to the good and the beautiful, even if our habitual self-addiction makes it look to us like a cold, dark void.

Isn't this the profound core of life itself, not only of Christianity and all human religions? It is the mystery of how happiness is found by surrendering the selfish desire for it, how love is released by self-forgetting, how life can only really blossom into boundlessness when it incorporates the actuality of death.

This message of Revelation presents us with a clear challenge: 'Purify your own soul and you cannot fail to purify your environment!' Greed, hate and delusion are the Beast, the enemy, and the battlefield whereon we can meet and defeat them is in our own heart.

A final plea: in working out new declarations for mobilising St John's message for today's victims of the environmental crisis, please make heroic hermeneutical efforts to reinterpret all forms of dualism that can anchor lethal exclusivisms: the split between humans and other animals, who can sometimes be thought to lack souls and therefore not to deserve the same fundamental consideration as other humans; the split between soul and body which can be shown to eventuate in malconsideration and mistreatment of women; the split between God and His Creation, which has demonstrably led to a destructive contempt and exploitive license with nature; even the split between the saved and the damned, which leads to lethal hatred of followers of other religions.

HH the Dalai Lama of Tibet always says that it is now too late in history for leaders or members of world religions to compete with each other for power and members - this only adds to the sources of conflict that abound in the world and proves right those who consider that religion itself is part of the problem. It is time for leaders or members of world religions to join in valuing the quality of the spirit, awareness, and action of individuals, rather than the denominational affiliation and to mobilise all their spiritual and inner scientific resources and co-operate together to help the secularists to cope with the terrible crises of our times, to stop the wars, share the wealth, preserve the environment, and further the material and spiritual welfare of all beings.

Ways forward:
hope for a better future

Introduction

Sarah Hobson

The formal proceedings of *Revelation and the Environment AD 95 - 1995* provided the intellectual framework for the symposium whereby invited contributors presented papers (reproduced in this book in Chapters 1 - 7) on particular issues relating to their area of expertise within an identified theme. The presentations offered stimulus for debate and discussion between participants whose knowledge bases were enriched by their varying religious beliefs and cultural perspectives. Having several days together on board a ship with limited on-shore visits meant that the pressures of time were distant and dialogue was often deep. Though their exchanges mostly went unrecorded - except in the memories of those participating - some of the issues and concerns were reflected in a series of informal interviews recorded on video by the film crew that was providing coverage of the symposium.

In their discussion, Professor Robert Thurman and Joel McCleary describe the apocalyptic interpretation by Christian fundamentalists in the USA today to justify the destruction of the environment and consider what impact a different interpretation would have, were it to be understood that the 'Apocalypse indicates the making of a new heaven and a new earth by God and therefore a positive end to history'. In contrast, Jojo Cariño, an Ibaloi Igorot from the Northern Philippines, shows how indigenous peoples are already successfully protecting their environment and how, if they could only be considered by others as 'people of the future' rather than 'people of the past', they could be called upon to contribute more substantially to the inter-cultural and inter-society dialogue on what is important for our times. The inclusion of indigenous peoples and respect for their rights consequently became one of the seven Patmos Proposals that were drawn up as a conclusion to the symposium, out of a need for action that would be carried forward by all the participants.

The presence of journalists and other representatives of the media at the symposium also created its own dynamic, since they needed to file stories that would be of interest to their editors and regular readers, listeners and viewers. Many had questions for the church leaders on board ship and a round table discussion was consequently organised whereby they could put their questions to a panel of five church leaders on the theme of 'The Church and the Environment'. It was an unusual event, with the church leaders speaking informally and openly on a range of issues that included population, sustainable development, war, environmental activism and hope for the future.

What can the Churches Offer?

A round table discussion with
His Beatitude Archbishop Anastasios of Albania
The Rt Revd and Rt Hon Richard Chartres, Bishop of London
His Eminence Cardinal Roger Etchegaray
His Grace Bishop Kallistos of Diokleia
His Eminence Metropolitan John of Pergamon

Reflections on the role of the Christian churches in encouraging concern for the environment

Archbishop Anastasios of Albania

I believe that it is important to cultivate the consciences of our people and that the church should become increasingly sensitive to issues concerning the environment. In order to have our people participating in the discussion of these issues, we have to find a common language, a common code of reference. That will be challenging for the people of the church, but I think that we have already begun the process. We have identified one problem as being indifference towards God's creation. One of our tasks is to make the people who come to church more aware that this passive attitude or indifference towards ecological issues is wrong and that they should become more appreciative of the integrity of creation, in other words the integrity of God's work. Although it would not be reasonable to expect results immediately, at least we have made a start. Fortunately in the church we live in hope and therefore we have the hope that we shall be more effective in the future.

Richard Chartres, Bishop of London

The churches, like everyone else, are still learning about an area in which there is a great deal of debate and discussion. While it would be appalling for churches to issue great calls without listening very carefully to the experts who are involved, it would also be very shocking if the churches simply espoused a dull echo of the liberal consensus, coming along behind to make the sort of predictable statements that could be heard from anyone else in life.

One of the great issues in our approach to the environment is how we perceive the world around us. If we perceive that world with our critical, estimating faculty, seeing it simply as an assembly of objects, then we will not generate the energy and love necessary to motivate us to look after and sustain our environment. In contrast, the churches' emphasis is on developing another way of perceiving and relating to reality. We see the world as a place where there is communion between different parts of creation and actual traffic between the creation and individuals; a place where there is the kind of knowledge and understanding that penetrates surfaces. This way of relating to other people and to the world around us is of astonishing environmental significance.

While the church may not be making great and complex statements about acid rain or other specific environmental issues, we are rediscovering an approach to creation which is crucial to everyone. This development of 'love' knowledge through meditation, prayer, spiritual discipline, restraint and sacrificial attitudes is the most practical approach we can take to the environment.

Metropolitan John of Pergamon

I certainly would like to think that Orthodox theologians are leading the rest of Christianity in this matter. There are indications that Orthodox theologians may have expressed their concern about ecological problems more than other churches, but we must be honest and realistic. For the moment concern for the environment is still very much an initiative or an attitude taken by the leadership of the church, and I'm afraid it has not yet really reached the congregations, filtered through to the church as a whole and become part of our theology. I think we are still very much at the beginning of the process. To take an example, in the Orthodox Church we still have not really absorbed the idea that there is such a thing as sin against the environment. If we asked the average faithful Orthodox in the street if he thought he had sinned that day by polluting the street, I doubt that he would honestly think of it as sin. We still have much work to do in the Orthodox Church in encouraging awareness of environmental issues.

Archbishop Anastasios

When we are focusing on what the church is doing about a particular problem, we must always remember that the church is not just the bishops, priests, deacons and those who have a specific leadership role. The church is all those who participate as responsible lay people in the eucharistic community. The fact is that there is already a sensitivity towards these issues among many lay people in the church; in other words the church is already participating in the debate. Furthermore, we began to discuss this issue of the integration of creation many years ago in the World Council of Churches so it is not something that the church has just recently discovered and is reacting to; on the contrary we have been engaged in the process for some time. Lay people have played a decisive role in this. Scientists who are at the frontiers of environmental research and those who make decisions in political and economic life, have been spokesmen for the church just as much as church leaders have.

Richard Chartres, Bishop of London

If it is the case that concern for the environment is a lay-led movement, that would be all to the good because of course the idea of the clergy as the officer class leading the lay people in the lower ranks is quite wrong. The Christian Church is the Truth of Jesus Christ embodied, and information and nourishment and spiritual energies move around that body. If lay people who are particularly alert to environmental issues are influencing church leaders, that is how the church ought to be operating; the church is not a management structure, it is an organism.

I think that all the churches have to be engaged in assisting each other to raise consciousness in this area. We have to be active in education; all our churches have a major stake in education. There have to be ways in particular of introducing young primary school children to the themes of the environment and their relationship to living a religious life in this world. There also has to be a cultivation of the disciplines of prayer and restraint, which will enable us to relate to one another and to the world in a more constructive way. That represents quite a programme to start with.

Metropolitan John of Pergamon

It is important that we take seriously the problem of evil. We very often convince ourselves that what is happening is not so bad, although I hope we are becoming increasingly aware of the seriousness of the situation. We often fail to realise that evil can lead to really apocalyptic, catastrophic situations. We have to learn from the book of the Apocalypse, what I call a liturgical outlook, namely that the world is a living organism which is entrusted to us so we can cultivate it in order to return it back to its creator. All these things will have to become part of our religious education. We ourselves have to enter into this process of education, because we do not tend to preach on these matters very much at all. They must become part of our theology, which at the moment does not really deal with them. The Christian Churches need to take the message of the Apocalypse very seriously with reference to these issues, and we should be trying to introduce these things into the consciousness of our faith.

Bishop Kallistos

I would agree with what was just said. I would simply like to add that there is one area where I would welcome a far clearer and more explicit witness by the churches in general and by the Orthodox Church in particular, and that is in the area of peace, warfare and the arms industry. We need to have a much more dynamic witness than we have now in favour of efforts towards peace.

Cardinal Etchegaray

The Catholic Church is not satisfied with just talking about ecology, it sees it as an integral part of the vision of the world that the church received from Christ and in a clear and vigorous way it seeks to put this vision before the consciences of the faithful.

As for the nuclear question, I am recently back from Western Samoa, where I was directly concerned with this issue, above and beyond nuclear testing. I am talking now not only on behalf of the Catholic state but on behalf of others. As the Pope has often said, we cannot consider the nuclear deterrent to be a workable solution in the long-term. The Catholic Church does not take a political stand on this. Perhaps we still think of it as a necessity, as in the time of the Cold War, but politicians must do everything in their power to overcome this hurdle of nuclear 'deterrent' as we are living on a mine field. The Catholic Church has no immediate practical solutions to offer, but it does indicate the direction to take and that is what counts.

Population control and the environment

Questioner

How does one reconcile church practices and rules on abortion and birth control with the experience of people of the church living in areas of dense population?

Cardinal Etchegaray

The problem is vast. It is a demographic and environmental problem. When the Pope speaks about this in particular, it is from the perspective of defending tooth and nail man and woman against himself and herself, to defend life from the perspective of the church's theological vision. What is important is to save life - life from before birth up until death. There is a logic from one end to the other along the path of life, from conception until death, and it is following the same path and the same logic that the current Catholic Church defends life, because life comes from God, it is in the hands of God, and we are not absolute masters of it.

Archbishop Anastasios

It is the clear conviction of the Orthodox Church that abortion is not a Christian option. We do not have the right to destroy life in this way. However in most parts of the Orthodox Church today a responsible use of birth control within marriage is allowed.

Bishop Kallistos

In the ancient world, parents had the right to kill their children if they were surplus to economic requirements or if they were feeble. It was under the Christian empire that infanticide of that kind became a criminal offence for the first time. This was one of the great changes brought about in the world by the Christian Church, a change powered by a huge reverence for life.

On a personal note, my brother was a person with a mental handicap and I owe almost all of my joy in life and my love of life to him. I am unable to contemplate the situation where, his incapacities having been discerned, he would have been removed from the scene, because he has been a most extraordinarily, potent influence on my life. Certainly responsible birth control within marriage can also be seen as part of a huge reverence for life, and I would take that point of view myself, but I would also stand very firmly against any trend which could turn the clock back in this respect. Reverence for life must be the keynote.

Cardinal Etchegaray

I would say that if a Christian is convinced that everything is created by God and is created at every level, not just man but all creatures, then he or she will find the real path to respecting all creation, be it mineral, vegetable or animal.

Sustainable development

Questioner

Does the monastic life offer a model of sustainable development and can it attract into the church those who have an interest in environmental issues?

Bishop Kallistos

My impression is that there is a great variety in monasteries. Among the Orthodox priests whom I know, the one who is most skilled in using a computer is a monk, and I think in today's world there are plenty of monks working with computers as well as growing cauliflowers!

Metropolitan John of Pergamon

I take a very positive view of monasticism and what it can contribute to the solution of our ecological problems, but I must say that there is a certain difficulty inherent in monasticism of which we have to be aware. It seems to me that monasticism, by traditionally laying stress on the spiritual aspect of life, does not always seem to be conscious of the seriousness of the ecological crisis. For example, on Mount Athos the monks do not realise that by throwing batteries into the open or into the sea they are seriously polluting the environment. I think even monks have to be educated ecologically. We should not take it for granted that because they are monks they are blameless in this respect.

Cardinal Etchegaray

Of course we cannot turn the whole world into a monastery, but in the tradition of all churches, monastic life is a reference point. Of course there are deviations, but ideally monastic life is like a micro-climate where creation can reach maturity.

The destruction of war

Questioner

War causes pollution not only to the environment but also to the souls of the people involved. The war in Bosnia involved Catholic and Orthodox Christians and Muslims. What is the position of the different churches represented at this panel on the war in Bosnia?

Archbishop Anastasios

This is yet another tragedy in our world, but the main factors are not to do with religious conflict. I believe that in this specific case, those responsible for the tragedy, educated in an atheistic system, have used religion as oil for their own fires. Religion is once again the victim in this story just as many innocent people are also victims of all these initiatives. The Orthodox Church has said many times that there is a real crime against innocent people being perpetrated here and the only thing we can do is to protest, to give voice to the voiceless, and to plead with the leaders of this tragedy, who do not speak for or represent religion, not to use it to fuel the situation.

Environmental activism

Questioner

Should the church be involved, like the environmental movement, in a practical way in lobbying, protesting and speaking out on specific issues? There is a tradition of this in some churches, for example among the liberation theologists in the Roman Catholic Church. Romaro in El Salvador has been very active in gathering together the parish priests to work on a particular issue and talk about it publicly in their churches. Would this be something the Orthodox Church would consider encouraging with regard to environmental matters? Would it be possible for church leaders in their own countries to convene meetings with environmentalists and to speak out in their parishes about the major problems of the environment?

Richard Chartres, Bishop of London

Many Christians are involved in lobby organisations and obviously from time to time churches attempt to bring pressure to bear by informal meetings and also by the weapon of boycott. However I think the most important attitude for us is to say, Lord we want a revolution, and may that revolution begin with me. I think that is our principal and first responsibility.

Cardinal Etchegaray

I think that the problem of ecology is directly related to spirituality - we cannot speak about material pollution without mentioning mental pollution, and this is the church's own role, to re-purify the mind because if we don't do that we cannot do the rest.

Metropolitan John of Pergamon

As far as I am concerned, the method that the church must use is to educate its people to behave responsibly. I do not think that we gain very much by these specific activities because the real problem goes much deeper. It is not simply a matter of how we solve this or that particular problem, it is more to do with how we change peoples' attitudes and mentalities. I would give greater priority and weight to that rather than to any other activity, as far as the church is concerned.

Questioner

Talking to many people across the world, one thing that the people in the developed world are missing in their life is ritual; the ritual of family life, the ritual of worship and especially of praise. We praise too many earth-people-made things rather than praising creation. Can the churches fill this gap which is lacking in so many people and help us to return to ways of thanking God for giving us this vibrant, living world on which we depend?

Metropolitan John of Pergamon

I want to endorse this point enthusiastically. Our communities and our societies have lost this liturgical part of life, and this is part of the problem. We must somehow recover this. The only thing that worries me is that, in order to have an effective ritual, you need a community to apply it, and I think communities today are diluted. We do not have communities in the old sense any longer - we have individuals and groups with various interests of their own. All this, to my mind, points to the necessity of recovering the community of the church as a community which has a cultural role to play. If we do that, then the ritual will become effective, otherwise it will just be a folklore which people will go to watch but which will have no effect on their lives.

Revelation: hope for the future

Questioner

This morning it was emphasised that the message of the Apocalypse is much more optimistic than most of us in the past have thought. Most environmentalists are very pessimistic in their analyses, though of course, when they have to conduct policies, they must conduct them in an optimistic way, whether or not they are believers. I would very much like to hear the bishops elaborate on this message of optimism coming from Apocalypse. I would also like to hear their comments on sin. Again, environmentalists feel a responsibility for cleaning up the accumulated pollution of others, so it is not only our own sin, but also the sins of others for which we are responsible. How does this relate to the idea of the sin of humanity against the environment?

Archbishop Anastasios

I think that the Book of Revelation has a very strong element of realism when it puts the emphasis on the battle with demonic powers. It is not an easy story, it is a real battle with victims, martyrs and heroes. The word *materia* is always a key word in it. It is a realistic approach, with an underlying theme and reality; God is the Alpha and the Omega, the One who is, who was and who is to come. This is what gives us hope. God is not the God of the past, but the God of eternity, and this idea is repeated again and again. At the end of the book there is victory, and the song of the new creation. The message is that there is indeed hope, but only after going through all these battles, tragedies and difficulties. I believe that keeping these eschatological and universal perspectives in mind is the key to understanding our present in a realistic way. It is most important, in order to maintain this hope, to act in the local situation while at the same time keeping the eschatological and the universal perspectives in mind. In doing so we really will be taking part in the concrete battle of this century. I don't like the words optimist or pessimist but I agree that we really do have a great and a real hope in the One who is, who was and who is to come.

Metropolitan John of Pergamon

I certainly agree that our optimism must be a realistic optimism, well aware of the battle that must take place, and also an optimism that derives from our faith in God, who was and is and will come. But as far as human responsibility and human activity are concerned, I think the Book of the Apocalypse also gives us the hope that there will always be at least a small remnant of people who will behave in the right way. Their optimism derives, of course, from their faith in God but also from their faith in what we call in theological language 'the community of sense', the knowledge that there will always be people who will think differently. In the typically Orthodox ascetic tradition we all have a share in universal sin, our own and the sins of others. Every monk is always conscious that he bears the sins of others, not simply his own sins. This is exactly what is happening in ecological terms. We are all called to bear the sinfulness of humanity as a whole and it is for that reason, in repentance and in vicarious behaviour, that I work to keep my environment clean on behalf of all those who pollute it. This sort of ethic, which comes from the book of the Apocalypse, is an important part of the ethos that we need today.

Cardinal Etchegaray

The role of the priest and archbishop is to make all his people vibrate to the symphony of creation. Every morning at Mass I address God, God of all Creation. I rejoice that in answering these questions we have been given the chance to find our feet on solid ground - or rather, at sea! - and be reminded of our spiritual responsibility. If I might summarise, all these problems, be they ecological, or ecclesiastical, point to a need for solidarity with the whole of creation. This is important for all of us. As our Albanian brother said, all Christian people must be conscious of their responsibility today towards the generations to follow, so that the creation of tomorrow will be even more beautiful than it is today, according to the image that God wished it to be.

Facing the Future with Hope: a Discussion from an American Perspective

Robert Thurman and Joel McCleary

Robert Thurman

There are some interesting similarities between the Apocalypse and the Buddhist Kalachakra Tantra. *Kalachakra* is a Sanskrit term meaning the wheel of time or the wheel of history. It refers to the notion of time as a kind of machine or wheel in which things are being developed to their own highest potential. This is as close as you could get to the monotheistic notion that history is God's crucible, within which beings are developed to the point of recognising their oneness with God. The Kalachakra prophecy predicts that earth will go through holocaust after holocaust as it moves into the future, but at a certain moment in history when it looks as if all is lost and materialism is in control, just as in the Apocalypse it looks as if the beast is in control, evolved, enlightened humans emerge and defeat the demonic or totalitarian dictatorial forces in a great battle, followed by a golden age on earth of several millennia.

Every culture, especially those which have experienced oppression and devastation, has a notion of apocalypse.

Joel McCleary

Don't you think that in America today the idea of apocalypse is a real, modern political phenomenon? Millions of people use the imagery of the Apocalypse in a very alive, political fashion and particularly in an anti-environmental context.

Robert Thurman

Many speakers at this conference have suggested that the Apocalypse indicates the making of a new heaven and a new earth by God and therefore a positive end to history. In a sense this creates a hopeful message about the environment. In America the very dominant Protestant (fundamentalist) interpretation is much more influential and this promotes an overwhelmingly anti-natural message, in which the text of Revelation is used to justify the destruction of the environment, because it is seen as a book of judgement. One of the great dangers of what is happening with the environmental movement in the United States is that those involved in it are portrayed by the fundamentalist Christian community almost as representatives of the anti-Christ and certainly as elitist and culturally out of step with the rest of America. That is why the message of this conference is so important - hearing major Christian leaders come out and say that there is no conflict between this text and the attempt to save the earth would be an explosive idea in America.

Joel McCleary

There are many popular paperbacks circulating in the United States which give very lurid interpretations of how America has the right to destroy everyone and everything, because that is what the Book of Revelation says is going to happen anyway. At different times different groups and leaders have been connected with the beast of Revelation - the Soviets, Iraq, for example, and now included in this list are liberals, including environmentalists and any other humane, welfare-oriented people. People around the world have no concept of how many people think like this in the United States and what a large political force they are.

I certainly hope that this conference will encourage line by line discussion of the text of Revelation and a wider audience for this more optimistic interpretation of the text from the churches represented here - Eastern Orthodox, Roman Catholic for example. It would create a real stir and a great dialogue in America if some of the very powerful ideas from this conference, such as that pollution is a sin, were advertised all across the country. It would be good if all the world's religious leaders could get together now and agree that, however we want to interpret the doctrine of the last judgement, or the Buddhist version of *Shambala,* or the Hindu version of *Kalki*, it is not to be used to justify the human destruction of the environment.

Robert Thurman

Shouldn't this be a spur for those who have heard this message to actively engage in politics and fight the battle for the environment?

Joel McCleary

Perhaps, but at the same time I think it would be interesting to get behind what people are saying at the conference to what they really think. Although they are talking optimistically, I wonder how many have an underlying pessimism. My guess would be that many people already feel that the time is too late, that we are already in the apocalypse, and in fact no-one is offering any really concrete solutions to the crisis. We are sitting around talking about what the architecture might be like in the new Jerusalem, and now we are all waiting with a great deal of faith to figure out how we get there.

Robert Thurman

That is exactly why it is so important for the liberal and environmentalist forces in the United States and world-wide to be active. I feel that the great temptation for them is the temptation of apathy, rising from a sense of the futility and the hopelessness of doing anything. You find this sense of disillusionment everywhere, even in American politics, the notion that liberalism is dead, that the government can't do anything. People believe that everything is hopeless so it's not worth trying to do anything about it; you might as well hide away and forget about it all.

Joel McCleary

I don't think that it is all hopeless. I think it is basically a spiritual problem rather than a political one. In the west we have gone through the industrial revolution, the material revolution, but we have no idea what to do with it. We have a fundamental pessimism in our outlook and what we need is a revolution in vision if we are to survive.

Robert Thurman

One of the most hopeful people I have heard in the conference, instead of talking about general principles, spoke about specific fishing communities and how their livelihood is destroyed by the overall situation. She pointed out that the developed world, the 20% of humanity that is consuming 80 % of the world's resources at a tremendous rate, are the ones who are continuously saying everything is hopeless. They (we) are saying that it is so hopeless that it is not worth trying to diminish their (our) own consumption. However, the people who are really facing the difficulties out there on the shores of the Malibar coast, with their fish running out because of enormous trawlers going by and sucking up the sea bottom, they cannot afford to be hopeless and pessimistic. They have to keep focused on scratching for what is immediately in front of them.

We are the ones who ironically could actually afford to do something about the situation by changing our diet, our transport/driving habits, our lifestyle, our politicians - if we were not so afraid of losing our luxurious lifestyle. That is why I believe that a valuable element of a conference like this has to be an increasing dialogue between people in the developed world and those in the so-called non-developed world, so that we can realise that in a way, although they are much poorer than we are, they actually have a much more positive and optimistic outlook on life which we could learn from.

Joel McCleary

One of the biggest problems that most people involved in politics have is trying to contain the appetite of the geometrically increasing population. The population explosion is coming at them so quickly, and the demands of that population are so immense and so hard to satisfy. It is almost like the Roman Circus - how can you feed the population of Rome and satisfy its appetite before it devours itself? The most articulate people in the world can talk about what needs to be done, but if no one wants to listen to them no wonder they are disillusioned. But we do not have the luxury of saying it is too late, we have to fight against that notion and keep moving forward.

It is a very real political problem though, because it is difficult to find the energy to bring about change and reform when it is hard enough work just trying to keep the system going. It becomes very hard to think even two or three years ahead, let alone two or three decades, which is what is needed at this point. We have already had our first war of immigration, in Haiti. That was the first time I know of in history where a country has invaded another country to stop that country's people from having a rationale to invade their border trying to find sanctuary. We are going to have to look more closely at the implications of doubling and tripling populations and the pressures that will bring.

Robert Thurman

On this question of population growth, the more optimistic people who are actually living in those places where the stress of population growth is greatest are always annoyed that the ones who make all the fuss about it are those who actually have enough food. The issues of wealth sharing and development need to be addressed. Big foundations will spend billions of dollars researching to develop some weird pill or magic bullet that will somehow solve the population explosion, but it has already been demonstrated that the one thing that has solved population growth in the world is wealth along with the education of women.

Joel McCleary

I agree totally on the subject of consumption. We need to look at what is being consumed right now by the 5 billion people in the world, and project to what it will be when there are 10 or 20 billion people. I am worried that there isn't a sufficient natural resource base for that size of population. I don't think we are always willing, at conferences like these, to admit our own real fears for the present and future. We need to be able to confront these fears head on and analyse their full implications. Then we need to have the courage to begin to share our visions of what the future will be like.

Robert Thurman

Sadly, there does not seem to be any constituency of support in America for doing the kind of moral, intelligent, enlightened or liberal things for the environment being suggested by people like Ambassador Timothy Wirth. Although many Americans say they are pro-environmental, they have elected people who are ready to sell every single environmental asset of the United States to exploiters, and who are ready to cancel any sort of assistance or reparations to any country they have ruined. In my opinion that is not so much a problem of apathy and lack of vision on the part of the American people, as a problem of lack of information, for which the media must take some responsibility.

I would like to see the new moguls of the information age providing real information, instead of hiding their heads in the sand. There could be true debate and discussion then, and a greater awareness of the need for a vision for the future.

Joel McCleary

I was told a wonderful story recently by Father Tom Berry who I think is the greatest environmental thinker in the Catholic Church in America today. He had just given his presentation at a big conference on the environment attended by all the Catholic bishops in Washington and all the top environmental thinkers. He presented an apocalyptic vision of what is happening and what the responsibility of the church has been. He spoke about the problem with the anti-nature interpretation that certain people have given to Christianity, which he believes to be a misinterpretation that must be dealt with if we are going to deal with the environmental crisis. Right at the end of his presentation a nun sitting at the back raised her hand and stood up.

'Father Berry,' she said, and she wrung her hands, 'I'm so depressed by what you have said, and I believe it is an accurate picture. But don't you think that at the end of the day God is going to save us?'

Father Berry, who is a rather controversial figure in the Catholic Church, reared back and in his full North Carolina accent said, 'What are you talking about? He'd just as soon shoot you as look at you. What do you think God is? Some kind of suburban pet that you can take out and walk around? You know you are totally mistaken. God is not going to save you.'

We need to deal with this issue of divine intervention. Is the ecological crisis simply a divine plan that is unfolding under God's control? Do we believe this is some kind of test for humanity, that we are being tested like Job? I think there is still a lot of confusion in the Christian world about this.

Robert Thurman

From the Buddhist point of view there is a way of seeing this as an elaborate test in the sense of an evolutionary challenge. For Buddhists the rationalisation of all this apparently senseless megadeath has to do with the continuing reincarnation of every being. It is not so much that beings die that matters, as how they die and how they are reborn. Buddhists do have a kind of apocalyptic faith in the omni-compassionate power of love and of enlightened beings to ensure that their deaths, rebirths and sufferings are always positive. Negative actions towards others, sin, violence, hatred, murder and greed, will result in violent, painful consequences rebounding from the environment. This continues to happen until beings develop the sensitivity not to harm other beings and that is how they evolve.

Buddhists have a problem with the Christian monotheistic vision because there is a big emphasis, particularly in the Book of Revelation, on excluding many beings from the new heaven and the new earth. Buddhists would want to encourage Christian leaders to move beyond finding exclusivist interpretations within the Bible and to come up with different interpretations. In moral language, even in Buddhism, there is a language of exclusivism which is intended to make people practice justice by threatening them with some sort of punishment. There is the feeling that if you are too forgiving, then there is the danger that people will indulge their evil appetites, believing that they will be forgiven later anyway.

The purpose of the picture of an unforgiving God presented by Father Berry to the nun is not to tell her that he does not have faith that she will be saved; instead he is trying to stimulate her to become part of the solution, to take some responsibility and action, rather than waiting to be saved by somebody else. But unfortunately some people interpret this talk about God saving us as an assurance that we'll be fine because we have a membership card, but we can let the rest of the world go down the drain. I believe that Christian leaders should not tolerate or promote this interpretation but should criticise it openly because it is lethal if we are thinking about caring for our environment.

Joel McCleary

There is another problem that we haven't considered. At the end of the twentieth century it is seems that all the -isms, all the big political theories, have collapsed - socialism, communism, and perhaps even Buddhism and Christianity. Unfortunately what has survived is tribalism. As the population increases and as the pressure on the immune system of Gaia increases, then people become survivalists. People get more and more pessimistic as they see the crisis approaching and they adopt a basic social Darwinian survivalist tribalist mentality, which is going to make it very difficult to deal with the environmentalist crisis. To use the language of Revelation, that may be the beast for us today.

We should look at what has actually happened in history. For example in Germany, the people had been through the first World War, the immense depression of the 20s, the disruption of German culture and society, the people had given up. In a kind of survivalist mentality they were willing to hand over their faith to Hitler to get them out of the situation, even if it was going to mean a lot of killing. They went along with the notion that very radical measures were necessary in order to survive. This is just like what we are seeing in Yugoslavia today - the same mentality, the idea that we are getting close to the apocalypse and religion has collapsed and there is no other positive ideology. The rationale for ethnic cleansing becomes the great race against time to survive at no matter what cost.

Robert Thurman

Yes, but you are leaving out two very important things. In the 30s the liberals and the socialists didn't even bother to vote. They believed they would come to power themselves when everyone saw how awful the fascists were. This is just like the present American electorate, where there is a large group of people, liberals among them, who do not vote for the same reason. The second point is that Hitler's government was the first to use the media effectively. Propaganda, television, modern information technology, the whole power of the media, were used to delude the German people. In the same way today the media in the United States are run by people who are in the grip of this self-destructive, exploitative mentality. This is what is convincing people that there is no hope. The counter media is not being heard.

Revelation still gives us hope. 'I heard a voice from heaven say unto me, Blessed are the dead which die in the Lord from henceforth. Yeah, sayeth His Spirit, that they may rest from their labours and their work, for their deeds will follow them' (Revelation 14:13). One way or another we are all going to die, even without an ecological crisis. It is unavoidable, whether it is in 10, 20, 30 or 50 years. The important thing is how we live and how we die. Socrates chose to drink hemlock, accepting the inevitability of death, rather than living by running away from Athens and becoming a fugitive, rather than living by dishonouring the laws of Athens, even if they were unjust. He was ready to die.

Now I'm going to bring you back to your disillusion with American politics and the issue of active involvement. Even in American politics I have noticed that people sometimes work all out, giving their hearts to do something better for the people, rather than just thinking about keeping people in office and preserving reputations. True, sometimes that fervour can diminish when people are in office, and a focus on simply surviving emerges, but my point is this: I feel there is room in politics for a leader or leaders, for inspirational people who can encourage us to think that radical change is possible. I believe that people sense that our times present enormous difficulties, and they are ready to be inspired. The strange thing is that anyone who wants to provide this inspiration will have to act in the spirit of the Book of Revelation and be willing to sacrifice themselves in order to do so.

A Practical Approach from the Philippines

Joji Cariño

The Igorot are a people numbering about one million in the north of the Philippines and the Ibaloi number about 75,000 in the southern part of the Cordillera. The Philippine government would refer to us as the indigenous cultural communities and we call ourselves the indigenous and traditional peoples of the Philippines. This is because, despite 300 years of Spanish colonial rule and about 50 of American rule, we have continued to maintain our economies and our cultures and control over our lands.

I work with Cordillera Peoples Alliance, which is a federation of community organisations in the Cordillera. I also work at the international secretariat of the International Alliance of Indigenous Peoples of the Tropical Forests, an intercontinental alliance of people who came together at the conference in 1992. We are trying to improve communication amongst ourselves and to become more effective in reforming international policy.

There is a great deal of environmental degradation in our world, but in fact if we look at areas where indigenous people are still in control of their land rights and resources, we can see that these are areas where, even if they are fragile, we have quite protected environments. If people are looking for sustainable alternatives, they are in fact still in existence and have been so since a long time ago in the past. For example there is a high correspondence between existing forests and the lands of indigenous peoples and also fragile but still viable environments where indigenous peoples are still in control. Destruction is encroaching on our lands and is affecting both peoples and environments but at the same time there are still large areas which are continuing to be viable today and which we feel should be appreciated and protected.

World-wide, people are realising the dangers of modern progress and are really beginning to understand its impact. Indigenous peoples have a longer history of the kinds of impact made by modern society, so while we are contemporary and have to cope with and deal with living in modern societies, at the same time we are more aware than others of the destructive impact this can have. We are trying to reach an accommodation and an understanding of ourselves as societies that are still viable, while being aware that there is no one road or one alternative to modernisation. In fact we acknowledge that there are several paths, and the fact that we are still viable means that it is worth looking at our societies and sharing our ideas with other modern societies.

Many Igorot are nominal or even practising Christians, because in parts of the Cordillera it is impossible to go to school unless you are baptised, but we also continue to practice our native religions. I myself continue to see the value of ancestral worship, which is our traditional religion. We pay homage to our ancestors and to the traditions and lessons that they have asked us to pass on. These are respect for the land, respect for elders and society and ensuring that there is not a great imbalance and fracture in society. I still believe in these viable and continuing truths.

It has been shown that the revival of our traditional beliefs has helped our community to cope with some of the difficulties of facing the modern world. Modern societies can learn from this revival. The challenge today is not just for indigenous peoples but also for modern societies. Those who are seeking ways forward into the Millennium usually look on us as people of the past, but I think what people have to understand is that we are really people of the future. If other societies are to have a future, then it will have to be a joint future, so I believe that this inter-cultural and inter-society dialogue and sharing is extremely important in our times.

If we break down this romantic, nostalgic notion that we are people of the past and realise that in fact we are contemporary people, then others will come to grips with living side-by-side with us and learning from us. The romantic attitude which says 'we have touched them, changed them and almost destroyed them, now let's regard them with reverence and nostalgia' is not the way to understand and live with indigenous peoples. In fact this nostalgia prevents people from coming face to face with indigenous peoples and actually bothering to listen directly to what they are saying. When contact is actually made and the effort is made to understand, then the nostalgia very quickly disappears, because indigenous peoples do not see themselves in a romanticised way and they are actually very forward looking.

Currently I am very involved with open cast mining. My people are traditionally small scale miners so we do engage in mining and do not call for a complete ban on it. Balitok is the guardian and the God of gold and in our stories he has told us that the wise approach towards gold is to have some but to be aware that when you are seduced by gold then it will destroy you as a person. Therefore he asks that whenever we get gold from the land we fulfil certain procedures so that we do not become seduced by it. Some stories say that Balitok completely destroyed the people when they did not follow his teachings and did not understand the power of gold over the community. Today, with the arrival of open cast mining, stories like this enable our communities to understand the seductive attraction of gold and the utter destruction this type of mining is going to cause, and they contrast this with the fact that we have been mining for centuries and still have our communities intact. The stories of Balitok have become very real. These kinds of beliefs and values need to continue to be used by our society even in this modern world.

Another example comes from another part of the Cordillera, among the Ifugao people, where there is a very long tradition of community forests. Certain trees are absolutely sacred and are not supposed to be cut down. Scientifically it has now been shown that these are water-bearing trees which have now been recognised as particularly important in terms of retention of the water which irrigates our rice terraces. There are many community sanctions for over-cutting the trees. Certain forest areas are reserved for certain clans and the clan is absolutely responsible, for example, for the outbreak of any kind of forest fire. Community sanctions are applied if a forest fire is permitted to occur in a clan's patch. For years now we have not had any problems with forest fires under this sort of community control, but now that the government is trying to say that these forests are national forests, forest fires are becoming a big problem because they are trying to remove control over the forest away from the community. Some people say that the forests are being set on fire almost as an expression of defiance. When community control is lost then problems of forest degradation rather than conservation start to occur.

The main use of water in our area is for irrigation of our rice terraces. Traditionally there has been a very highly developed system of community control and co-operation over the use of water. It is a very valuable resource because we are land locked and do not have access to the seas, so our water comes mainly from the rivers in the Cordillera. However all the rivers of the Luzon area emanate from the Cordillera and damming in that area has became a big problem for us - because all of the rivers come from our mountains.

The Cordillera is very densely populated for a mountain region and it is quite remarkable that it has been able to continue terracing the land and feeding its people in what is quite a fragile environment. In many places in the world small subsistence farmers are actually better off than the urban poor. It would be very sad if the future brought a move to the cities, due to the loss of our land and the supposed seductive attraction of city life. Communities like ours can actually point a way forward for modern societies and can give us hope for the future.

The Patmos Proposals: Seven Steps for Action

David Shreeve

So there we sat, five virtual strangers, our ship anchored in a small Turkish port and although late it seemed wrong to call it a day.

An American, a Persian, German and two English. Put another way - a marine scientist, a lecturer, two environmentalists and a journalist. On another level we included a Roman Catholic, Protestants and a Zoroastrian.

In other words, a pretty mixed bunch who found ourselves sharing the pleasure of watching a moon we all knew reflected on a sea surrounding a coast which made us all strangers.

Our talk not unnaturally turned to the one thing we had in common - the Patmos cruise. We were, after all, experiencing something quite unique and it would be only natural to wonder why and how we came to be part of it.

Then the discussion turned to what could possibly be achieved by the exercise and what we as individuals or as a group might be able to contribute.

This is how the Patmos Proposals came about. In fact during that balmy hour or so around midnight little more than the idea was discussed, but in its limited state it did seem like a good constructive idea. We knew that the number seven had a major significance in the story of the Apocalypse - so all we needed to do was come up with the seven ways the talking on the boat could be turned into positive action for the future.

At breakfast later that morning enthusiasm still remained and was increased with the support of David Bellamy. It was agreed that we should put our idea to the organisers and offer to develop it. Our chosen prey was the Bishop of London who grasped the nettle immediately and instantly created a quorum which he then announced to the assembling delegates at the start of the morning session. From here on meetings were held and suggestion boxes produced so that participants in the symposium could contribute their ideas. It was clear that many of them wanted proposals for action.

By the time the boat returned to Piraeus, burning the midnight oil had still not produced the Proposals in the form we all wished and so thanks to faxes and emails on dry land and across other channels and oceans we finished our task and circulated to all participants *The Patmos Proposals: Seven Steps for Action.*

The Patmos Proposals: Seven Steps for Action

In response to the Ecumenical Patriarch's invitation to participate in the symposium *Revelation and the Environment* delegates have produced the following proposals for him to consider in formulating his response to the growing concern for the future of the world's environment.

The delegates believe that in his support for the symposium, and the very positive atmosphere it achieved, the Patriarch can act as a leader not just in his, but for other religions to encourage global environmental awareness crucial to achieving a sustainable environment on earth.

1. **A New Sense of Sin.** All religions affirm as an imperative, the need to care for the Earth and for the whole of nature. To pollute the environment or not to take care of it should be seen as sin. This new sense of sin extends beyond what has been traditionally considered wrong.

   This new category of sin should include activities that lead to:

   - species extinction
   - reduction in genetic diversity
   - pollution of the hydrosphere, lithosphere, and atmosphere
   - eutrophication of the hydrosphere, lithosphere, and atmosphere
   - habitat destruction
   - disruption of sustainable lifestyles.

   Specific examples discussed at the conference include:

   - the imminent extinction of the Monk Seals
   - continued abuse of the Black Sea.

2. **Recognise and support the rights of traditional communities** - recognising that indigenous peoples are the architects and stewards of sustainable management, the guardians, and in the case of crop plants and animals, the creators of biodiversity; we urge churches, scientists and environmentalists to support the cause of indigenous peoples and traditional communities throughout the world.

   Examples:

   - protection of their lands
   - protection of their ways of life

• recognition of their property rights.

3. Recognising the lack of environmental knowledge in many levels of society, the Church should **encourage the development and implementation of education programs** for audiences from all schools (including Sunday Schools) to adult (including seminary).

   Examples:

   • 'Green Bible'

   • a series of publications linking the religions of the world to their natural heritage

   • at baptisms/weddings stress parental environmental responsibilities.

4. Recognising that the improvement of information exchange between Church, NGOs and government on environmental matters is of crucial importance, the Church should **encourage efforts at planning, collaboration, and co-operation** whenever and wherever possible.

   Examples:

   • each church should appoint official environmental contacts at all levels of their organisation especially local churches

   • support at least one major co-operative project for the Millennium such as the rehabilitation of the Black Sea, Aegean Sea, for example.

   • encourage governments to involve the public in all aspects of natural resource management

   • the island of Patmos (not just its ecological centre) could become an environmental showpiece.

5. Responding to the need for clear leadership, **the Church should take positive steps in establishing sustainable and environmentally-friendly land-use practices, resource use and investments.**

   Examples:

   • issue guidelines for sustainable use and best practice for all church lands

   • all new or renovated religious edifices utilise the most efficient energy conservation and waste reduction and disposal technologies

   • establish nature reserves or afforestation projects on all appropriate church properties

• all Church investments should be in 'green' or environmentally friendly sustainable businesses or investment portfolios.

6. Recognising the vital role that the world's media could play in promoting awareness of environmental issues, the Church should **encourage the media to feature environmental issues on a more sustained and regular basis.**

   Example:

   • make space on a regular basis to encourage environmental awareness and sustainable activities in all publications from parish newsletters to national and international press and television.

7. Recognising the urgency of the Earth's environmental problems, projects **promoting the Patmos Proposals are of utmost urgency**. They could include:

   • establishment of a Green Award(s) by the Church for, for example, a scientist, or environmental activist

   • develop a Church outreach environmental agency (Orthodox NGO)

   • institutionalise celebratory tree planting (birth, wedding, death)

   • all faiths to promote a green will/trust option

   • establishment of a cruising environmental educational vessel that would promote the Patmos Proposals.

Ad hoc committee members: David Bellamy, Shahin Bekhradnia, Lynne Carter, Alexander Goldsmith, Michael Hanssler, David Shreeve

Profiles of contributors

Editors

Sarah Hobson

Sarah Hobson is a writer and filmmaker, who for many years has provided a channel for people to communicate the reality of their changing circumstances to a wider world from many different cultures and religious backgrounds. Working in villages in Iran, India, West Africa, and the Andes, she has an understanding of how people combine their sense of the sacred with the practical needs of survival. She has direct experience of the relationship between religion and the environment among rural communities that are Christian, Muslim, Zoroastrian, Hindu, Buddhist and Sikh. She is currently director of Open Channels, a non-profit making organisation that works to empower local communities through a strategic approach to communication and information.

Professor Jane Lubchenco

Professor Jane Lubchenco was a member of the Scientific Committee for *Revelation and the Environment AD 95 - 1995.* She is Professor of Zoology at Oregon State University, a Pew Scholar in Conservation and the Environment and a MacArthur Fellow. She is President-elect of the American Association for the Advancement of Science and a Past President of the Ecological Society of America. Her interests include conservation biology, biodiversity, ecological causes and consequences of global changes, and sustainable ecological systems. She co-chairs the SCOPE sustainable Biosphere Project, an interdisciplinary scientific programme designed to propose environmentally sound policy and management options for seven regions of the world.

Contributors

Professor Daniel Amit

Professor Daniel Amit was born in Lodz, Poland in 1938 and received his Ph.D. in physics from Brandeis University in 1966. Professor of Physics at the University of Jerusalem and the University of Rome, La Sapienza. Chairman Racah Institute of Physics 1984-1987. Author of *Fields Theory and Critical Phenomena* (McGraw-Hill) and *Modelling Brain Function* (Cambridge).

Professor Mehmet Aydin

Professor Mehmet Aydin was born in Turkey in 1943, graduated from Ankara University, Faculty of Theology in 1966, received his Ph.D. in Philosophy from

Edinburgh University in 1971, became Associate Professor in 1978 and a full Professor in 1984. He taught at AtatŸrk University, Erzurum, 1971-1973; at Ankara University and Middle East Technical University, 1976-1984; and has since been teaching at Dokuz EylŸl University, where he is Dean of the Faculty of Divinity. Member of the Council for the Institute of Post-Graduate Studies. Member of the Turkish Philosophical Association. Author of *God and Moral Value in Kant and in Modern British Philosophy*, 2nd ed. Ankara, 1992; *Turkish Contribution to Philosophy*, Ankara, 1985; *Philosophy of Religion*, 3rd ed. Ankara, 1992; and *Religious Culture and Moral Knowledge*, Ankara, 1982.

Shahin Bekhradnia

Shahin Bekhradnia was born in London of traditional Iranian Zoroastrian parents. As a main part of her religious upbringing, issues concerning pollution of the air, land and water entered her consciousness at an early age, long before such matters had been taken up by the media and before environmental organisations came into being in Britain. After taking a degree in Modern Languages at Oxford, she worked in Iran and then travelled round the world before returning to found a sixth-form and language college in Oxford. Her fascination with history and her encounters with people of different faiths and cultures focused her interest on the processes of identity formation, out of which emerged a doctoral thesis in anthropology at St Anthony's College, Oxford, on 'Identity Change among Iranian Zoroastrians in the 20th Century', on which subject she has lectured and published regularly. Most recently her research has focused on the Pamir Mountain area in Tajikistan. In recent years interfaith activities have taken some of her time and she has been actively involved with environmental organisations and issues for many years, both at village and national level, having contested district council elections and a General Election as a Green candidate.

Professor David Bellamy

Professor David James Bellamy, OBE, BSc, PhD, DSc, D Univ, DScHon, FLS, F.I.Biol., F.I.Env Sci., FRGS, FZS, is a botanist, ecologist, author, broadcaster and consultant. Honorary Professor of Adult and Continuing Education, University of Durham - ongoing. Special Professor of Botany, Nottingham University - ongoing. Visiting Professor of Natural Heritage Studies, Massey University, New Zealand, 1988/89. Founder Director, The Conservation Foundation, London. Director, David Bellamy Associates, now part of PE International. President of Population Concern, Youth Hostels Association, WATCH, National Association of Environmental Education, Plantlife, Surrey Wildlife Trust, Cleveland Wildlife Trust. Chairperson of the Trustees Saving Bank's Committee dealing with its Environmental Unit Trust Fund. Patron of Soil Health Association of New Zealand. Patron of the West Midlands Youth Ballet.

Founder Director of the New Zealand Natural Heritage Foundation. Professor Bellamy is the author of 84 scientific papers and 43 books, and the writer and presenter of over 400 television programmes on ecology and the environment. He has been awarded the Dutch Order of the Golden Ark, 1989, and the CNNA Award and the UNEP Global 500 Award in 1990.

Professor John Broome

Professor John Broome is Professor of Economics and Philosophy at the University of Bristol. He works in areas where economics and ethics come together; he applies formal techniques from economics to ethical theory, and he examines ethical questions raised by economics. One of his interests - combining ethics and economics - is the value of the environment. Among his books are *Weighing Goods* (Blackwell, 1991) and *Counting the Cost of Global Warming* (White Horse Press, 1992). He is now working on *Weighing Lives,* which deals with the value of extending people's lives and the value of adding new lives to the population.

Joji Cariño

Joji Cariño is an Ibalot-Igorot, from the Cordillera region, northern Philippines and a committed writer, learner-educator and campaigner on indigenous peoples' rights. She was active in the Kalinga and Bontoc people's successful struggle to stop the building of four massive dams along the Chico River in the 70s and 80s. She was imprisoned under the Marcos martial law government and adopted as prisoner of conscience by Amnesty International. She works with the Cordillera Peoples Alliance, a regional federation of Cordillera indigenous organisations, serving as international representative in Europe. Current Cordillera campaigns include open-cast mining and erosion of indigenous agricultural systems. She co-ordinates Cordillerra Links, a London-based education and advocacy project committed to local autonomy, cultural diversity and building international solidarity between Igorot peoples and other peoples of the world. Joji Cariño is Indigenous Policy Adviser with the International Alliance of Indigenous-Tribal Peoples of the Tropical Forests. Founded at an indigenous conference in Penang in 1992, this is an intercontinental network of indigenous-tribal peoples' organisations from tropical forest countries, bringing together people from central and south America, west and central Africa, south and south-east Asia and the Pacific.

The Rt Revd and Rt Hon Richard Chartres

The Rt Revd and Rt Hon Richard Chartres, Bishop of Stepney, was born in 1947. He was ordained in 1973 and after his curacy became chaplain to Robert Runcie when he was Bishop of St Albans and then travelled widely with him as chaplain to the

Archbishop of Canterbury. Before his consecration in May 1992 as Bishop of Stepney he worked for eight years as a parish priest at St Stephen's, Rochester Row near Victoria in London. For six years he was Gresham Professor of Divinity in the City of London (1986-1992). He is married to Caroline and they have four children: Alexander, Sophie, Louis and Clio (all under 9). He is Ecclesiastical Patron of the Prayer Book Society and has recently become Chair of the Anglican-Russian Orthodox Liaison Group. Areas of interest outside the church are the Ancient Mediterranean world, its art and literature, French and Russian culture and language, and anything to do with the East End of London.

Professor Herman E Daly

Professor Herman Daly is currently Senior Research Scholar at the University of Maryland, School of Public Affairs. From 1988 to 1994 he was Senior Economist in the Environment Department of the World Bank. Prior to 1988 he was Alumni Professor of Economics at Louisiana State University, where he taught for twenty years. He has served as Ford Foundation Visiting Professor at the University of Ceara (Brazil), as a Research Associate at Yale University, as a Visiting Fellow at the Australian National University, and as a Senior Fulbright Lecturer in Brazil. He has served on the boards of advisors of numerous environmental organisations, and is co-founder and associate editor of the journal *Ecological Economics* (Elsevier). He is co-author with theologian John Cobb of *For the Common Good; Redirecting the Economy Toward Community, the Environment, and a Sustainable Future,* Beacon Press (1989,1994); and author of *Steady-State Economics*, Island Press (1977,1991).

Professor Constantine Despotopoulos

Professor Constantine Despotopoulos, born in 1913, was Minister of Education in two Greek governments, in 1989 and 1990. He has been a full member of the Academy of Athens since 1984 and served as its President during 1993. He was a regular lecturer in Philosophy as a full Professor of the Pantion University in Athens until 1980. During the years of political upheaval in Greece he was Professeur Associé at the French University Nancy II (1969-1974). He is Honorary President of the Greek Philosophical Society and served as its President. He is an Honorary Member of the Romanian Academy and a Foreign Member of the Academy in Marseilles. He has published many books, in Greek, in French and in English. The more important of them are, in English: *Philosophy of History in Ancient Greece* (Athens, 1991); in French: *Etudes sur la liberté* (Paris, 1974), *Aristote sur la famille et la justice* (Brussells, 1983); in Greek: *Philosophy of Law* (1954), *Political Philosophy of Plato* (1957), *Ethics* (1962), *Studies in Philosophy* (1965), *Studies in Political Philosophy* (1975), *Studies in Philosophy II* (1980), *Literary Essays* (1981), *Philosophy and Dialectic* (1990).

Dr Charles N Ehler

Dr Charles Ehler is the Director of the Office of Ocean Resources Conservation and Assessment (ORCA) within the National Oceanic and Atmospheric Administration (NOAA). He is responsible for managing NOAA's coastal assessment programs, including hazardous materials response, natural resource damage assessment, coastal pollution monitoring, and national assessments of coastal resource use and conservation. Recently, he co-ordinated scientific support during the $1 billion response to the Exxon Valdez oil spill in Alaska, and was deeply involved preparing the natural resource damage assessment and negotiating the $2 billion settlement with the Exxon Corporation for damages to natural resources caused by the spill. He has worked for NOAA for almost 18 years, for the US Environmental Protection Agency's Office of Research and Development, and taught natural resources planning and management at the University of Michigan, the University of California at Los Angeles, and the State University of New York at Stony Brook.

Cardinal Roger Etchegaray

Cardinal Roger Etchegaray was born at Espelette, in the French section of the Basque country, in 1922. His father was a watchmaker and agricultural mechanic. He was ordained a priest for the diocese of Bayonne in 1947 and then received a licenciate in theology and a doctorate in canon law from the Gregorian University, Rome. Much of Cardinal Etchegaray's early priestly ministry was at the direct service of the diocese, finally as Vicar General of the Diocese (1960). In 1960, he was named Associate Secretary General of the French Episcopal Conference, then Secretary General (1966 to 1970). He served as an expert at the Second Vatican Council. In 1969, he was ordained a Bishop and named Auxiliary Bishop of Paris. Very shortly afterwards, he became Archbishop of Marseilles (1970-1984). He was president of the French Episcopal Conference from 1975 to 1981. The inspiring force behind foundation of the Council of Episcopal Conferences of Europe, he became its first president (1971-1979) and, in this capacity, travelled widely in Central and Eastern Europe. He was named a Cardinal by Pope John Paul II in June 1979 and then called to Rome in 1984 to be President of both the Pontifical Council for Justice and Peace and the Pontifical Council Cor Unum (responsible for the co-ordination of the Church's charitable and aid services). In addition to his countless trips across the world for the two Councils he heads, Cardinal Etchegaray has visited many of the most troubled spots of the world at the direct request of the Holy Father: Iran and Iraq, Lebanon, Mozambique, Angola, Ethiopia, Sudan, South Africa, Cuba, Haiti, Central America, Vietnam, Myanmar (Burma), the former Yugoslavia, Liberia, Rwanda and Burundi. The Cardinal also has other responsibilities within the Roman Curia. He is a member of the Congregations for Oriental Churches, for the Evangelization of Peoples, for Catholic Education as well as of the Supreme

Tribunal for the Apostolic Signatory. He is also a member of the Presidency of the Pontifical Council for the Laity and of the Pontifical Councils for the Unity of Christians, for Inter-Religious Dialogue, for Social Communications as well as of the Administration of the Patrimony of the Holy See. He also belongs to the Commission for Dialogue with the Oriental Churches. Finally, on 15 November 1994, the Holy Father announced the formation of a Central Committee for the Jubilee of the Year 2000 and named Cardinal Etchegaray its president. He is a member of the Academy of Social, Moral and Political Sciences of the French Academy since December 1994, and was the first recipient of the international ecumenical prize Ladislaw Laszt, created by the Israeli Ben Gourion University. Cardinal Etchegaray is the author of several books: *Dieu à Marseille* (1976), *J'avance comme un âne* (1984), *L'Evangile aux couleurs de la vie* (1987).

Rev Alexander Fostiropoulos

Born in Thessaloniki, Greece in 1952, Father Alexander Fostiropoulos studied at the Architectural Association School of Architecture in London (1972-1978) and worked as an architectural consultant-designer for the next seven years. He was ordained deacon in 1980 and a priest in 1985 at the Russian Orthodox Cathedral in London. Since his ordination to the priesthood he has also been the Orthodox Chaplain to the University of London based at Kings College, London and at the London School of Economics. From 1988 to 1993 he was Co-Secretary to the Orthodox-Anglican Theological Commission under the Orthodox Chairmanship of Metropolitan John of Pergamon. He is also the priest responsible for the Orthodox community in Canterbury, Kent, England. Father Alexander has worked extensively with youth camps and with Syndesmos (The World Fellowship of Orthodox Youth), has four children aged eight to fifteen with his wife Patricia, and lives in London.

Professor Ioannis M Fountoulis

Professor Ioannis Fountoulis was born in 1927. He studied Theology at the University of Athens, with post-graduate studies at the University of Louvain in Belgium where he also received instruction in Liturgy as well as in the History and Philology of Eastern Christian Liturgy. He also studied Liturgy in Trier, Germany. Professor Fountoulis is currently Professor of Liturgics and Homilectics in the Theological School at the University of Thessaloniki, and director of the Patriarchal Institute for Patristic Studies in Thessaloniki. He has published a number of papers on liturgical themes.

Edward Goldsmith

Edward Goldsmith was born in Paris in 1928, holds dual British and French nationality and was educated at Millfield School and Magdalen College, Oxford (M.A. in Politics, Philosophy and Economics). He has been publisher of *The Ecologist* since 1969, and was also its editor from 1969 to 1990. He is the author of *The Stable Society* (1978), *The Great U-Turn* (1988), and *The Way: An Ecological World-View* (1992); co-author of *A Blueprint for Survival* (1972), Vol 1 of *The Social and Environmental Effects of Large Dams* (1984), and *5,000 Days to Save the Planet* (1990); editor of *Can Britain Survive?* (1971); and co-editor of Vols II and III of *The Social and Environmental Effects of Large Dams* (1986, 1992), *The Earth Report* (1988), *Gaia, the Thesis, the Mechanisms and the Implications* (1988), and *Gaia and Evolution* (1990). Edward Goldsmith taught courses on ecology and related subjects at Michigan University (1975) and Sangamon State University (1984), and is still working with a Global Ecology Course which he set up in 1990 with the International Honors Programme, associated with Bard College. He is Vice-President of Ecoropa, and President of Ecoropa, France, a Member of the Praesidium of the Vienna Academy for Future Studies, Director of the Schumacher Society, Principal Environmental Consultant to the Goldsmith Foundation, and Trustee of the Foundation for Gaia. He received the Honorary Right Livelihood Award (known as the alternative Nobel Prize) in 1991 and was in the same year made a Chevalier de la Legion d'Honneur.

William S Hatcher

William S Hatcher is a mathematician, philosopher and educator. Born in 1935 in Charlotte, North Carolina, USA, he holds a Doctorate in Mathematics from the University of Neuchâtel, Switzerland, 1963, a Master's from Vanderbilt University, 1958, and a B A *cum laude* from Vanderbilt University, 1957. A specialist in the philosophical interpretation of science and religion, he has, for over thirty years, held university positions and lectured widely in North America, Europe and Russia, where he now resides and works. He is the author and co-author of over fifty professional articles, books and monographs in the mathematical sciences, logic and philosophy. Among his works are *The Logical Foundations of Mathematics,* Pergamon Press, Oxford, 1982; *The Baha'i Faith* (co-authored with J. Douglas Martin), Harper and Row (now Harper Collins), 1984 (designated as a 'book of the year' in religion by Encyclopaedia Britannica, 1986); *Logic and Logos,* George Ronald, Oxford, 1990 (a resumè of this latter work is included in the *Encyclopèdie Philosophique Universelle,* Presses Universitaires de France, 1992, where Professor Hatcher is listed as one of eight Platonist philosophers of the second half of the twentieth century) and *The Law of Love Enshrined* (co-authored with John Hatcher), George Ronald, Oxford, 1996.

Sir John Houghton

Sir John Houghton CBE FRS was born in 1931 and educated at Rhyl Grammar School and Jesus College, Oxford. From 1958-1983 he was successively lecturer, Reader (1962) and Professor (1976) in the Department of Atmospheric Physics at Oxford University when he became well known internationally for his outstanding research in remote sensing of the atmosphere from space. In 1979, Sir John was seconded from Oxford University to the Science and Engineering Research Council to be Director of the Appleton Laboratory during its merger with the Rutherford Laboratory. From 1983 to 1991, he was Director-General (later Chief Executive) of the UK Meteorological Office. In 1988 he was appointed as Chairman of the Scientific Assessment Working Group of the Intergovernmental Panel on Climate Change (IPCC) jointly set up by WMO and the UN Environment Programme. The first Assessment by that Working Group on the likely change in climate during the next century due to the increasing release of greenhouse gases into the atmosphere was influential in forming a scientific basis for the Framework Convention on Climate Change (FCCC) agreed at the Earth Summit in Rio in 1992. After retiring from the Meteorological Office in 1991, Sir John became Chairman of the Royal Commission on Environmental Pollution in the UK and in 1994 he was appointed a member of the UK Government Panel on Sustainable Development. His many honours and awards include Fellowship of the Royal Society (1972), Symons Gold Medal of the Royal Meteorological Society and the Gold Medal of the Royal Astronomical Society. He has published over a hundred scientific papers on radiation transfer, remote sensing and climate change, and authored or co-authored a number of books including *The Physics of Atmospheres*, 1977 (2nd edition 1986); *Global Warming: the Complete Briefing*, 1994 (runner-up for the Sir Peter Kent Conservation Book Prize 1995); and *The Search for God, can science help?* in 1995.

Chief Vaasiliifiti Jackson

Chief Vaasiliifiti Moelagi Jackson was born in 1942 on one of the most beautiful of the Western Samoan islands in the South Pacific, and with her husband founded in 1976 the first hotel on Savaii, which has a population of 55,000. Among groups she has helped to establish is the Faasao Savaii Society, the country's first rural conservation organisation. She was founder of the Safua Eco-Tourism Programme, under which individual families and villages are helped to develop so as to host visitors in non-intrusive ways which generate funds for the local community. She also founded and is currently Vice President of the Western Samona Umbrella for Women NGOs, and is still the owner and general manager of the Safua Hotel, Tour Office and Eco-Tourism Programme.

Bishop Kallistos of Diokleia

Bishop Kallistos of Diokleia (Timothy Ware) was born in Bath, England, in 1934 and was educated at Westminster School, London and at Magdalen College, Oxford. At university he studied classical languages, philosophy and theology and he received the degree of D Phil for his dissertation on St Mark the Monk and the early history of eastern monasticism. In 1958 he joined the Orthodox Church and in 1966 he was ordained priest and took monastic vows at the Monastery of St John the Theologian, Patmos. Since 1966 he has been Spalding Lecturer in Eastern Orthodox Studies at the University of Oxford and in 1970 he became a Fellow of Pembroke College, Oxford. In 1982 he was consecrated bishop. His books include *The Orthodox Church* and *The Orthodox Way*. He is co-translator of two Orthodox service books, *The Festal Menaion* and *The Lenten Triodion*, and also of the five-volume English edition of *The Philokalia* (four volumes so far published).

Metropolitan John of Pergamon

The Most Rev Metropolitan John of Pergamon was born in 1931. He studied at the Theological Schools of the Universities of Thessaloniki and of Athens, graduating from the latter in 1955. After extensive studies abroad, he submitted his doctoral thesis to the Theological School of the University of Athens and became a Doctor of Theology in 1965. For three years he was Secretary of the Faith and Order section of the World Council of Churches in Geneva. He taught Dogmatic Theology for three years at the University of Edinburgh and was Professor of Systematic Theology at the University of Glasgow for 14 years. Visiting Professor to the University of Geneva, London University and Grigorian University, Rome he has been a participant in many international scientific conferences and has for many years represented the Ecumenical Patriarchate on international church bodies and on special ecclesiastical missions. He is a member of the International Committee for formal Theological Dialogue with the Roman Catholic Church and Orthodox President of the International Committee for Theological Dialogue with the Anglican Church and was a member for eight years of the Central Committee of the World Council of Churches and of the Faith and Order Committee of that body as representative of the Ecumenical Patriarch. Author of many scientific studies in various languages and Honorary Doctor of the Catholic Institute of Paris and the Orthodox Theological School, Belgrade, he was elected 1973 as a member of the International Academy of Religious Science in Brussels. He was appointed Metropolitan in 1986 and elected regular member of the Athens Academy in 1993.

Graeme Kelleher

Graeme Kelleher trained as a civil engineer, a profession which he practised in the design and construction of major water supply projects in Australia and Canada for 20 years. For the past 20 years he has been engaged in environmental and natural resource management both nationally in Australia and internationally. He was Chairman and Chief Executive of the Great Barrier Marine Park Authority between 1979 and 1994 and has been Vice Chairman (Marine) of IUCN's Commission on National Parks and Protected Areas since 1986. In the latter position he has been responsible for establishing the foundation for a Global Representative System of Marine Protected Areas. This system is designed to protect habitats which represent all the major bio-geographic zones of the world's coastal seas. Among various other positions, Graeme Kelleher has occupied the Kevin Stark Chair of Systems Engineering at James Cook University, Townsville since 1992. He is a Member of the Order of Australia and a Fellow of the Australian Academy of Technological Sciences and Engineering and of the Institution of Engineers, Australia.

Dr Üner Kirdar

Dr Üner Kirdar was born in Turkey in 1933. He graduated from the Faculty of Law, Istanbul, with post graduate studies at the London School of Economics, and received his PhD from Jesus College, Cambridge. Dr Kirdar has served the United Nations in various capacities. Currently, he is Senior Advisor to UNDP Administrator and the Special Representative of the Secretary-General of Habitat II in New York. He was the Secretary of the UN Conference of Human Settlements, Habitat I, in 1976; Director of External Relations and Secretary to the Governing Council of UNDP from 1980 to 1991. A main architect of the UNDP Development Study Programme, he has also held senior positions in Turkey's Ministry of Foreign Affairs, including that of Deputy Permanent Representative of Turkey to the UN Office in Geneva. He is author of *Structure of UN Economic Aid to Underdeveloped Countries* (Marinus Nijhoff, 1966, 1968) and editor, co-editor, and contributor to more than sixteen books on the human dimension of economic, social, and environmental development.

Professor Alexandre Kiss

Professor Alexandre Kiss is of French and Hungarian nationality, was born in Budapest in 1925, and has lived in France since 1947. Director of research emeritus at the Centre National de la Recherche Scientifique (France), Professor at the Robert Schuman University of Strasbourg and the Law School of the University of Santa Clara, California, Professor Kiss is President of the European Council for Environmental Law, Vice-President of the International Institute of Human Rights, Vice-Chair of the Commission of Environmental Law of IUCN and President of Environement sans frontière. Consultant with all the international organisations involved with environmental protection, he has lectured and contributed to conferences in almost all European countries, in North America, in various Latin American and African countries, in Japan, etc. Publications include books on general international law, human rights law and since 1973 mainly on international environmental law; he has published approximately 350 articles on the same subjects. He has been awarded the Cross of Officer of the Legion d'Honneur (France) and the Austrian Distinguished Merit Cross and is a Member of the Hungarian Academy of Sciences.

Rahmi M Koc

Rahmi M Koc was born in Ankara, Turkey in 1930 and is the Chairman of the Board of Directors of Koc Holding A S, a Fortune 500 company with 1994 sales of approx. $ 6.3 billion and employing 33,000 people. A graduate in Business Administration from John Hopkins University, he has spent all his business career in Turkey with the family-owned holding company in which he represents the second generation. Among his wide-ranging philanthropic and other commitments, he is Chairman of the Board of the newly founded Koc University and of the American Bristol Hospital; the founder and Chairman of Turmepa, (Turkish Marine Environment Protection Association); Chairman of the Turkish-Greek Businessmen's Association; President of the International Chamber of Commerce; Member of the Centre for Strategic and International Studies (CSIS), and of the Advisory Boards of Chase Manhattan Bank in New York and of the American University in Washington DC.

Bo Erik Olaf Krantz

Bo Krantz was born in Sweden in 1939, and majored in Business Administration from Stockholm University, with postgraduate studies in the US at Cornell University. He started out with Skandinaviska Banken (1960-1962), and was then with the Scandinavian Airlines Group through to 1987, where he was successively Economics Manager SAS Sweden, Director Group Financing, Vice President Finance and then President, Nyman & Schultz Travel, and from 1984 President Business Travel System. Between 1987 and 1988 he was Executive Vice President of PK Banken and then President of PK Partner. Between 1988 and 1990 he was Senior Vice President of Stockholm Saltjon AB, and has since 1990 been Secretary General of Stockholm Water Foundation, founded in that year by the City of Stockholm and a number of Swedish industrial groups to promote efforts to improve water conservation through the world.

Geoffrey Lean

Geoffrey Lean, the Environment Correspondent of the *Independent on Sunday*, has specialised in the environment and development for 25 years and holds many awards for his work. Born in 1947 he has a B A in Modern History from Oxford University. He joined the *Yorkshire Post* in 1969, moved to *The Observer* in 1977 and then to the *Independent on Sunday* in 1993. He has been a consultant to the World Bank, the United Nations Development Programme and the Food and Agriculture Organisation and has written and edited many reports for the United Nations Environment Programme; since 1994 he has been the external editor of UNEP's magazine, *Our Planet*. He is the author of *Rich World Poor World* (1978) and general editor of the *Atlas of the Environment* (1990, 1992). His awards include being runner-up as Britain's Young Journalist of the Year (1972), the Communication Arts Award of Excellence (1986), a UNEP Global 500 (1987) and the Schumacher Award (1994). He is the only journalist ever to have been given the British Environment and Media Awards' premier Awareness Award for consistent achievement (1991), and is consistently voted 'most impressive environmental journalist in Britain' by his peers in an annual poll.

Professor Jane Lubchenco

Professor of Zoology at Oregon State University, a Pew Scholar in Conservation and the Environment and a MacArthur Fellow, Professor Jane Lubchenco is President-elect of the American Association for the Advancement of Science and a past President of the Ecological Society of America. She was named Oregon Scientist of the Year in 1994 and is a member of the American Academy of Arts and Sciences. A marine ecologist by training (PhD from Harvard University), Professor Lubchenco's interests include conservation biology, biodiversity, ecological causes and consequences of global changes, and sustainable ecological systems. She led innovative efforts of the Ecological Society of America to set national priorities for ecological research, an endeavour which resulted in the Sustainable Biosphere Initiative, and she co-chairs the international SCOPE Sustainable Biosphere Project, an interdisciplinary scientific programme designed to propose environmentally sound policy and management options for seven regions of the world. Named Outstanding Teacher of the Year at Oregon State University in 1986, Dr Lubchenco has collaborated several times with James and Elaine Larison to produce educational scientific films; their most recent efforts have included *Oregon's Oceans*, a PBS film, and *Diversity of Life*, a National Geographic Society film which won a CINE Golden Eagle Award. She is a member of the Boards of Directors of World Resources Institute, the Environmental Defence Fund, Northwest Environment Watch, and Colorado College. Professor Lubchenco also serves on advisory committees for the National Research Council, the National Science Foundation, the National Park Service and the UN Environment Programme. Her husband Dr Bruce Menge, also a marine ecologist, is Professor of Zoology at Oregon State University.

Alastair McIntosh

Environmental consultant/Edinburgh University

Joel McCleary

Joel McCleary was born in 1948 and received a BA at Harvard University, 1971. He was treasurer, Democratic National Committee, 1977 to 1978, and White House Assistant to the President, 1978 to 1980. He served as President, Sawyer-Miller International, 1981 to 1989, and was President of the Institute of Asian Democracy, 1990 to 1992.

Dr Laurence D Mee

Dr Laurence Mee is a specialist in environmental science and policy, currently engaged as the Co-ordinator of the Global Environment Facility's Black Sea Environmental Programme. He was born in Ipswich, England in 1951. He received a Bachelor's degree in Chemistry with Honours in Oceanography from the University of Liverpool in 1974 followed by a Doctorate in Chemical Oceanography from the same University in 1977. His postgraduate research included work off the West Coast of Africa and in Mexico where he studied coastal lagoon ecosystems. Dr Mee worked for ten years as a researcher and Professor in the National Autonomous University of Mexico in Mazatlan and Mexico City, travelling extensively in Latin America and researching in marine fertility and geochemistry. Following earlier brief assignments in the United Nations, he took up the full time position of Head of the Marine Environmental Studies Laboratory, IAEA Marine Environment Laboratory in Monaco in 1987. The Laboratory, the only one of its kind in the UN system, was responsible for providing technical support to regional pollution assessments. The work included pesticides studies in Central America, the first survey of the impact of the Gulf War, pollution studies in the Caribbean, Mediterranean, Danube River and Black Sea as well as the training of young specialists. In 1991, he participated in the group which prepared the final document (Agenda 21) for the Rio Conference, the largest ever gathering of Heads of State. In 1991 he assisted the Black Sea governments to draft the Odessa Ministerial Declaration on the Protection of the Black Sea and to request support from the newly-formed Global Environment Facility for a three year Black Sea Environmental Programme (BSEP) to help improve technical capacity, environmental policy and investments in the Black Sea ecosystem. He joined the United Nations Development Programme in 1993 and was appointed as Co-ordinator of the BSEP. The BSEP has enabled the drafting of the Black Sea Action Plan, a long-term strategy of profound reforms adopted by all six governments of Black

Sea countries. Dr Mee is a Fellow of the Royal Society of Chemistry, a full Member of the Ukrainian Academy of Ecological Sciences and Honorary Member of the Georgian Academy of Ecological Sciences.

Professor Paul Mendes-Flohr

Professor Paul Mendes-Flohr is a Professor of Modern Jewish Thought and Intellectual History at the Hebrew University of Jerusalem. He is the co-editor *of The Journal of Jewish Thought and Philosophy* and *Hebräsche Belträge*. He has written or edited numerous books, including *Divided Passions, Jewish Intellectuals and the Experience of Modernity* (1992); *Correspondence of Martin Buber* (1992); *Gershom Scholem: The Man and His Work* (1993) (with Jehuda Reinharz); *The Jew in the Modern World. A Documentary History*, (2nd ed. 1995). He is the former Chair of the Rainbow Group, a Jerusalem Interfaith Fraternity.

Professor Norman Myers

Professor Norman Myers is an independent scientist in environment and development. He has worked since 1970 on a variety of issues such as mass extinction of species, tropical forests, environmental economics, population, global warming, and environmental security, all within a context of sustainable development. He has undertaken this work for the US National Academy of Sciences, the World Bank, United Nations agencies, US Congress, the White House, the Smithsonian Institution and the World Resources Institute, among many other organisations. His main professional interest lies with the interface between scientific research and public policy. His publications include more than 200 papers in professional journals and a number of books: *The Sinking Ark* (Pergamon Press, Oxford and New York, 1979); *Conversion of Tropical Moist Forests* (National Research Council, Washington DC, 1980); *A Wealth of Wild Species* (Westview Press, Boulder, Colorado, 1983); *The Primary Source* (W W Norton, New York, 1984); *The Gaia Atlas of Planet Management* (Doubleday, New York, and Pan Books, London, 1985); *The Gaia Atlas of Future Worlds: Challenge and Opportunity in an Age of Change* (Doubleday, New York, and Robertson McCarta, London, 1990); *Population, Resources and Environment: The Critical Challenges* (Banson Books, New York, 1991); *Ultimate Security: The Environmental Basis of Political Stability* (W W Norton, New York, 1993) and *Scarcity or Abundance: A Debate on the Environment* (with J Simon, W W Norton, New York, 1994); *Environmental Exodus: An Emergent Crisis in the Global Arena* (Climate Institute, Washington DC, 1995). Professor Myers is a Visiting Fellow of Green College, Oxford University, and a Visiting Professor at Cornell University, The University of Utrecht and the University of Kent. He is a Senior Fellow of the World Wildlife Fund - US. He has lectured at more than one hundred universities and colleges in the United States.

He is a Foreign Associate of the US National Academy of Sciences, a Fellow of the American Association for the Advancement of Science and of the World Academy of Art and Science, and has been elected to the UNEP Global 500 Roll of Honour. He was awarded the 1992 Volvo Environment Prize, the largest award of its kind outside the United States. Professor Myers' books have sold over one million copies in all and are printed in eleven languages.

Dr Andreas A Papandreou

Dr Andreas A Papandreou is a research fellow and lecturer on environmental economics at University College London, and a member of the Centre for Social and Economic Research on the Global Environment (CSERGE). He has also been a fellow at the Stockholm Environment Institute (SEI), a visiting Assistant Professor at Franklin and Marshall College, Pennsylvania, and held a post-doctorate fellowship at Harvard University. He is the author of *Externality and Institutions* (OUP, 1994). He received his doctorate degree in Economics from Merton College, Oxford University.

Dr K L Seshagiri Rao

Dr K L Seshagiri Rao, Professor Emeritus of Religious Studies at the University of Virginia, is widely considered to be one of the world's leading scholars on Hinduism, Gandhian Studies and on interreligious dialogue, and has written many books, and numerous articles in professional journals addressing various aspects of these subjects. Dr Rao earned his bachelor's and master's degrees from the University of Mysore in India, and received his Ph.D. from Harvard University, where he studied at the Center for the Study of World Religions. He has lectured extensively and participated at symposia and conferences around the world including serving as co-Chair of the World Council of Churches International Hindu-Christian Consultation in 1981. Dr Rao worked as Professor of Comparative Religion and Chairman of the Department of Religious Studies, Punjabi University, Patiala, India before he moved in 1970 to the University of Virginia in the United States. He has also taught as visiting Professor at the University of California, Santa Barbara, CA and at Washington and Lee University, VA. Till January 1995 he worked as Professor of Religious Studies at the University of Virginia, Charlottesville, VA. He has served as Vice President of the World Hindu Federation, based in Kathmandu, Nepal; President of the International Association of Gandhian Studies, headquartered in Philadelphia; and as Vice-president of QUEST Institute, Charlottesville, VA. He is an advisor of the Center for World Thanksgiving, Dallas. Dr Rao is a co-editor of *World Faiths Encounter*, a foremost interfaith journal published by the World Congress of Faiths, London, and is the chief editor of the 18-volume *Encyclopedia of Hinduism*.

Professor Vandana Shiva

Professor Vandana Shiva was born in 1952, trained as a physicist and did her PhD on the subject 'Hidden Variables and Nonlocality in Quantum Theory' from the University of Western Ontario. She later shifted to inter-disciplinary research in science, technology and environmental policy. She is Director, Research Foundation for Science, Technology and Natural Resource Policy, Dehra Dun; Director, Navdanya - a seed conservation project; Advisor, Third World Network, Penang; Consultant, FAO, New Delhi; and Visiting Professor, Schumacher College, England, and University of Oslo. She is a member of the National Environmental Council, Government of India and of the Advisory Board, University Grants Commission, India; Convenor, Core Group of Experts, National Action Plan on Biodiversity, Ministry of Environment, Government of India; and Co-Chair, Women, Environment and Development Organisation. Significant books Dr Shiva has published include: *Monocultures of the Mind: Biodiversity, Biotechnology and Agriculture,* Third World Network, Penang and Zed Press, U.K.; *Cultivating Diversity: A people's programme for biodiversity conservation in agriculture* and *Sustaining Diversity: Renewing diversity and balancing through conservation*, Research Foundation for Science, Technology and Natural Resource Policy, Dehra Dun, 1993; *Women, Ecology and Health: Rebuilding connections* (Editor), Dag Hammarskjold Foundation and Kali for Women (1993) and *Closer to Home*, Earthscan, London, 1994; *Ecofeminism,* Kali for Women, New Delhi and Zed Books, UK, 1993; *Biodiversity: Social and Ecological Perspectives* (Editor), Third World Network, Penang, Zed Press, UK, 1992; *Ecology and the Politics of Survival*, UNU, Tokyo and SAGE, New Delhi and London, 1991; *The Violence of the Green Revolution: Ecological degradation and political conflict in Punjab*, Third World Network, Penang, Zed Press, UK, 1991; *Staying Alive: Women, Ecology and Survival in India,* Kali for Women, New Delhi 1988, Zed Press, UK (translated into five other languages). She was honoured in 1993 with the Order of the Golden Ark; election to UNEP Global 500 Roll of Honour; the Earth Day International Award; the Alternative Nobel Peace Prize (Right Livelihood Award); and the VIDA SANA International Award.

David Shreeve

David Shreeve founded the Conservation Foundation with David Bellamy to provide a link between industry and the environment by creating and managing environmental schemes often supported by commercial organisations. Although originally limited to the UK, the Foundation has since developed a wide-ranging programme ranging from Russia to rain forests. David is now the Foundation's executive director and editor of its publication *Network 21.* He previously worked in public relations.

Dr Rajwant Singh

Dr Rajwant Singh was born in Calcutta, India, in 1961 and did his schooling in Calcutta. He emigrated to the US in 1979 and completed a Doctorate in Dental Surgery in 1989 from the School of Dentistry, Georgetown University, Washington, DC. He helped initiate the Sikh Association of America, a national Sikh body in 1984, and is a founding member of the Guru Gobind Singh Foundation, which has initiated the Sikh community's participation in many inter-faith activities. Currently Dr Singh is the President of the Interfaith Conference of Metropolitan Washington, which for the last fifteen years has been bringing together seven world faith traditions for dialogue and joint action on critical issues in the metropolitan area. Dr Singh has since its inception been a board member of the North American Interfaith Network, which brings together 65 local and national interfaith organisations for networking. Dr Singh provided the Sikh readings on the environment in the publication of the United Nations Environment Program for the Environment Sabbath. He also represented the Sikh faith at the Global Forum for Human Survival in Moscow in 1990 which focused on saving the Earth's ecology. He serves as the special advisor on environmental issues to Jathedar Manjit Singh, the Spiritual Head of the world-wide Sikh community. He also wrote the Sikh faith's viewpoint on the environment and presented it in Japan at the Summit on Conservation and Religions. Recently Dr Singh has initiated the formation of a network of Sikh organisations in North America which will help co-ordinate activities focused on education and other critical issues facing the community. He is also President of the North American chapter of the International Human Rights Organisation of the Indian Sub-continent, and works closely with other world human rights bodies.

Dr Laxmi Mall Singhvi

Dr Laxmi Mall Singhvi was born in 1931 and educated at the Universities of Allahabad (BA), Rajasthan (LLB), Cambridge, Harvard (LLM), Cornell (SJD). He is married and has a son and a daughter. A career jurist, he was elected as a Lok Sabha MP (1962-1967), was Deputy Leader of the Indian Delegation to the 1964 Commonwealth Party Conference and has served on numerous all-party and on Government of India Committees including that on Information and Broadcasting Media (1964-1967) and on Revitalisation of Rural Local Self-Government (1986-1987). A senior advocate, Supreme Court of India since 1967, he was president of the Bar Association (1978-1982). He has served *inter alia* as Secretary General of the 4th Commonwealth Law Conference 1971, Chairman of the World Colloquium on Legal Aid, London 1975, was founder in 1979 and has since been president of the Indian Centre for the Independence of Judges and Lawyers, was Vice Chairman of the UN Human Rights sub-committee,1981, and President of the World Congress on Human Rights 1990-present. He led India's Human Rights Delegation to UN Conferences in Bangkok,

Geneva and Vienna (1993), was a founder member of the Family Planning Foundation of India, and is president emeritus of the Authors' Guild of India, of which he was president 1985-1990. He has been Indian High Commissioner to the Court of St James since 1991. His books include *Horizons of Freedom* (1969), *Law and Poverty* (ed. 1970), *Indian Federalism* (1974), *Law Day* (1979), *Legal Aid* (1985), *Independence of Justice* (1985). Dr Singhvi has been awarded the Interfaith Gold Medallion Award by the International Council of Christians and Jews; was appointed President of the Council to the World Parliamentary Religions held in Chicago in 1993; and was leader of the Jain delegation to the International Conference on Religion and Conservation of Environment held at Mount Fuji, Japan and Windsor Castle, UK, March-April 1995.

Professor Robert Thurman

Professor Robert A F Thurman, a college professor and writer for twenty years, holds the first endowed chair in Indo-Tibetan Buddhist Studies in America. He has been a student of Tibet and Tibetan Buddhism for almost thirty years, and is a close personal friend of HH the Dalai Lama. He has written a number of books, both scholarly and popular, and has lectured widely all over the world. Father of five children, he takes a special interest in exploring the Indo-Tibetan philosophical and psychological traditions to discover whatever universal insights into the human heart might be most useful to people caught in the daily crises of modern life. He also takes seriously the responsibility of members of 'developed' societies today to act to preserve the planetary environment, along with the life of the alternative forms of human civilisation, such as the Tibetan, that have become so deeply endangered. Professor Thurman has been Jey Tsong Khapa Professor of Indo-Tibetan Buddhist Studies, Columbia University since 1988, and President since 1992 of Tibet House New York, of which he was in 1987, and remains, a Founding Trustee.

Dr Dalibor Vesely

Dr Dalibor Vesely was born in Prague, and studied Architecture in that city, and Art History and Philosophy in Prague and Munich. Before 1968 he worked as a designer and consultant and as a Research Fellow in the Academy of Sciences in Prague. He then emigrated to the UK, where he taught Design at the Architectural Association in London and History and Philosophy of Architecture at the University of Essex. He was Visiting Professor at Princeton, in 1975 and at Harvard in 1982. He has been in Cambridge, UK, since 1978 teaching Design in the Diploma Studio and is a Head of the Post Graduate Programme in the History and Philosophy of Architecture. He was in 1991 one of the founding members of the Central European University in Prague, and of the Department of Advanced Studies in Art and Architecture where he is a permanent Visiting Professor. Dalibor Vesely publishes and lectures internationally on the topics of Anthropology and Hermeneutics of Architecture, the Problems of Representation and the Poetics of Architecture.

Timothy E Wirth

Timothy Wirth was born in 1939 in Santa Fè, New Mexico, and is US Under Secretary of State for Global Affairs, with responsibility for co-ordinating a broad group of global programs, including population, environment, science, counternarcotics, democracy, human rights and refugees. From 1987-1993 Mr Wirth was US Senator from Colorado, but chose not to run for re-election. In the Senate he was particularly engaged in natural resource issues, writing successful energy, conservation and environmental protection legislation, and the Colorado Wilderness Bill. He drafted the first comprehensive global climate change bill and, with Senator Alan Simpson, introduced the first bi-partisan population legislation. With the late Senator John Heinz, he co-authored Project 88, a ground-breaking framework for using market forces to achieve environmental goals. He served as co-chairman of the Clinton-Gore presidential campaign. His wife Wren is president of the environmentally committed Winslow Foundation.

Professor Christos Yannaras

Professor Christos Yannaras was born in Athens in 1935. His university studies were Theology in Athens, Philosophy both in Bonn (Germany) and Paris (France), and he is a Doctor of Theology, University of Thessaloniki, and a Doctor of Philosophy, Facultè des Lettres et Sciences Humaines, Sorbonne (Paris). Dr Yannaras is a Visiting Professor to the Russian Theological Institute, Paris; to the Ecumenical Institute (Catholic University), Paris; to the Theological School of the University of Geneva; to the Theological School of the University of Lausanne; and to the Philosophical School of the University of Crete. Since 1983 he has been Professor of Philosophy, Panteion University of Social and Political Science, Athens. He is a member of the Academie Internationale des Sciences Religieuses, Brussels. Representative publications include: *Haidegger and Aeropagita* (1968), *The Freedom of Morality* (1972), *Personhood and Eros* (1976), *Suggestions on Critical Ontology* (1985), *Rationality and Social Praxis* (1986), *The Real and the Imaginary in Political Economy* (1990), *Meta-modern, Meta-physics* (1993). Dr Yannaras's books have been translated into Russian, Finnish, Italian, French, German and English.